2018 SQA Specimen and Past Papers with Answers

Higher
CHEMISTRY

2017 & 2018 Exams
and 2018 Specimen Question Paper

HODDER
GIBSON
AN HACHETTE UK COMPANY

This book contains the official SQA 2017 and 2018 Exams, and the 2018 Specimen Question Paper for Higher Chemistry, with associated SQA-approved answers modified from the official marking instructions that accompany the paper.

In addition the book contains study skills advice. This advice has been specially commissioned by Hodder Gibson, and has been written by experienced senior teachers and examiners in line with the Higher syllabus and assessment outlines. This is not SQA material but has been devised to provide further guidance for Higher examinations.

Every effort has been made to trace the copyright holders and to obtain their permission for the use of copyright material. Hodder Gibson will be happy to receive information allowing us to rectify any error or omission in future editions.

Hachette UK's policy is to use papers that are natural, renewable and recyclable products and made from wood grown in sustainable forests. The logging and manufacturing processes are expected to conform to the environmental regulations of the country of origin.

Orders: please contact Bookpoint Ltd, 130 Park Drive, Milton Park, Abingdon, Oxon OX14 4SE. Telephone: (44) 01235 827827. Fax: (44) 01235 400454. Lines are open 9.00–5.00, Monday to Saturday, with a 24-hour message answering service. Visit our website at www.hoddereducation.co.uk. Hodder Gibson can also be contacted directly at: hoddergibson@hodder.co.uk

This collection first published in 2018 by
Hodder Gibson, an imprint of Hodder Education,
An Hachette UK Company
211 St Vincent Street
Glasgow G2 5QY

Typeset by Aptara, Inc.

Printed in the UK

A catalogue record for this title is available from the British Library

ISBN: 978-1-5104-5717-1

2 1

2019 2018

Introduction

Higher Chemistry

The Course

The main aims of the Higher Chemistry course are for learners to:

- develop and apply knowledge and understanding of chemistry
- develop an understanding of chemistry's role in scientific issues and relevant applications of chemistry, including the impact these could make in society and the environment
- develop scientific analytical thinking skills, including scientific evaluation, in a chemistry context
- develop the use of technology, equipment and materials, safely, in practical scientific activities, including using risk assessments
- develop scientific inquiry, investigative, problem solving and planning skills
- use and understand scientific literacy to communicate ideas and issues and to make scientifically informed choices
- develop skills of independent working.

How the Course is assessed

There are two parts to the Higher Chemistry assessment:

1. An assignment worth 20% of your overall course mark
2. A multiple choice exam and an extended-response exam, worth 80% of your overall course mark

You will carry out your assignment during class time and write a report, summarising your findings, under exam conditions. Your report will be marked by the SQA and contributes 20% to the overall course mark.

The course award is graded A–D, the grade being determined by the total mark you score in the examination and the mark you gain in the assignment.

The Examination

The written exam comprises two question papers: a multiple choice exam worth 25 marks, and an extended-response paper, worth 95 marks. You will be given 40 minutes to answer the multiple choice questions and 2 hours 20 minutes to answer the extended-response questions. Overall, the written exams contribute 80% to the overall course mark.

Key Tips For Your Success

Practise! Practise! Practise!

In common with Higher Mathematics and the other Higher sciences, the key to exam success in Chemistry is to prepare by regularly answering questions. Use the questions as a prompt for further study: if you find that you cannot answer a question, review your notes and/or textbook to help you find the necessary knowledge to answer the question. You will quickly find out what you can/cannot do if you invest time attempting to answer questions. It is a much more valuable use of time than passively copying notes, which is a common trap many students fall into!

The data booklet

The data booklet contains formulae and useful data, which you will have to use in the exam. Although you might think that you have a good memory for chemical data (such as the symbols for elements or the atomic mass of an element) always check using the data booklet.

Calculations

In preparation for the exam, ensure that you recognise the different calculation types:

- relative rate
- using bond enthalpy
- using $cm\Delta T$
- percentage yield
- atom economy
- using molar volume
- volumetric calculations
- calculations from balanced chemical equations

You will encounter these calculations in the exam so it's worth spending time practising to ensure that you are familiar with the routines for solving these problems. Even if you are not sure how to attempt a calculation question, show your working! You will be given credit for calculations, which are relevant to the problem being solved.

Explain questions

You will encounter questions, which ask you to *explain your answer*. Take your time and attempt to explain to the examiner. If you can use a diagram or chemical equations to aid your answer, use these as they can really bring an answer to life.

Applying your knowledge of practical chemistry

As part of your Higher Chemistry experience, you should have had plenty of practice carrying out experiments using standard lab equipment and you should have had opportunities to evaluate your results from experiments. In the Higher exam, you are expected to be familiar with the techniques and apparatus listed in the tables below.

Apparatus

Beaker	Dropper	Pipette filler
Boiling tube/ Test tubes	Evaporating basin	Distillation flask
Burette	Funnel	Thermometer
Conical flask	Measuring cylinder	Volumetric flask
Delivery tubes	Pipette	Condenser

Techniques

Distillation
Filtration
Methods for collecting a gas: over water or using a gas syringe
Safe heating methods: using a Bunsen, water bath or heating mantle
Titration
Use of a balance, including measuring mass by difference
Determining enthalpy changes

The following general points about experimental chemistry are worth noting:

- A pipette is more accurate than a measuring cylinder for measuring fixed volumes of liquid. A burette can be used to measure non-standard volumes of liquid.

- A standard flask is used to make up a standard solution i.e. a solution of accurately known concentration. This is done by dissolving a known mass of solute in water and transferring to the standard flask with rinsings. Finally, the standard flask is made up to the mark with water.

- A gas syringe is an excellent method for measuring the volume of gas produced from an experiment.

- Bunsen burners cannot be used near flammable substances.

- A Bunsen burner does not allow you to control the rate of heating.

Analysis of data

From your experience working with experimental data you should know how to calculate averages, how to eliminate rogue data, how to draw graphs (scatter and best fit line/curve) and how to interpret graphs.

It is common in Higher exams to be presented with titration data such as the data shown in the table below.

Titration	Volume, cm^3
1	28.0
2	21.1
3	21.0
4	21.2
5	34.0

You should be able to look at a table of titration results like this and conclude:

(a) Titration 1 is a rough result.

(b) Titrations 2, 3 and 4 are concordant, i.e. they are within $0.2\,cm^3$ of each other.

(c) The average titre is the sum of all concordant results divided by the number of concordant results. In this case, average titre = $\frac{21.1 + 21.0 + 21.2}{3} = 21.1\,cm^3$

(d) Titration 5 is a rogue result or outlier, probably caused by experimental error.

Numeracy

The Higher Chemistry exam will contain several questions that test your numeracy skills e.g. calculating relative rate, enthalpy changes, percentage yield etc. Other questions will ask you to "scale up" or "scale down" as this is a skill that is used by practising scientists in their day to day job.

Being able to deal with proportion is key to answering numeracy questions in chemistry. A common layout is shown in the examples below. In all cases, the unknown (what you are being asked to calculate) should be put on the right hand side.

[Example]

The enthalpy of combustion of ethanol is $-1367\,kJ\,mol^{-1}$.

Calculate the theoretical amount of energy that could be released by burning 10 g of ethanol.

Solution

This question is about proportion. A good way to tackle such a question is to establish a relationship between two quantities and then scale to 1. Here, the relationship is between mass (since we are asked about 10 g) and energy.

Whatever you are asked to calculate (in this case energy) put it on the right-hand side, i.e.

Mass ➡ Energy

Since you are told that the energy is $-1367\,kJ\,mol^{-1}$, you should be able to calculate the mass of ethanol since the energy is for 1 mol = GFM. For ethanol, 1 mol = 46 g.

Step 1: Establish a relationship

46 g ➡ $-1367\,kJ$

Step 2: Scale to 1

1 g ➡ $\dfrac{-1367}{46} = -29.717\,kJ$

Step 3: Calculate for the quantity you are asked.

10 g ➡ $10 \times -29.72 = \underline{\textbf{−297.17\,kJ}}$

[Example]

A 100 ml bottle of children's paracetamol costs £3.85. The ingredients label states that each 5 ml dose contains 120 mg of paracetamol. Calculate the cost per mg of paracetamol.

Answer:

Volume		Mass
5 ml	➡	120 mg
1 ml	➡	24 mg
100 ml	➡	2400 mg

i.e. 1 bottle contains 2400 mg of paracetamol

Mass		Cost
2400 mg	➡	£3.85
1 mg	➡	£0.0016

Open-ended questions

Real-life chemistry problems rarely have a fixed answer. In the Higher exam, you will encounter two 3 mark questions that are open-ended, i.e. there is more than one "correct" answer. You will recognise these questions from the phrase *using your knowledge of chemistry* in the question. To tackle these, look at the following example.

[Example]

Carbon compounds contribute to our everyday lives as chemists have discovered their usefulness in making foods and cosmetics. Using your knowledge of chemistry, comment on the type of carbon compounds that are likely to be found in food and cosmetics.

Your answer should include typical structures and explain some properties of the compounds which relate to their use.

Author's suggested answer

The beauty of an open-ended question like this is that there are so many carbon compounds you could discuss. The key to answering this question is to think about the carbon compounds you encountered in National 5. Then, think about some of the reactions or properties which would make them useful for the areas mentioned.

As the question states, you should detail your answer with typical structures so that you can show the examiner that you know your chemistry!

The table below lists *some* compounds you could discuss with some details of properties you could mention.

Compound	Comments on properties	Typical structure
Esters	Often have fruity tastes so used as flavourings. Often have pleasant smells so can be used in perfumes etc. You could discuss the fact that esters are non-polar so can dissolve non-polar compounds, e.g. used as the solvent in nail varnish.	
Aldehydes and Ketones	Flavour molecules found in foods. Used as solvents for cosmetics.	
Carboxylic acids	Ethanoic acid is the acid found in vinegar. Has a specific taste.	
Antioxidants	Antioxidants, such as vitamins C and E, are added to food and cosmetics to prevent the food/cosmetic oxidising.	
Soaps	Long chain hydrocarbons (hydrophobic) with a carboxylate head (hydrophilic) which can remove greasy stains.	

You would not be expected to cover all these compounds. A good answer could cover just two examples but would give lots of details on the compounds' properties and structures.

You could also discuss alcohols, detergents, emulsifiers, terpenes, etc.

Good luck!

If you have followed the advice given in this introduction you will be well prepared for the Higher exam. When you sit the exam, take your time and use the experience as an opportunity to show the examiner how much you know. And good luck!

Study Skills – what you need to know to pass exams!

General exam revision: 20 top tips

When preparing for exams, it is easy to feel unsure of where to start or how to revise. This guide to general exam revision provides a good starting place, and, as these are very general tips, they can be applied to all your exams.

1. Start revising in good time.

Don't leave revision until the last minute – this will make you panic and it will be difficult to learn. Make a revision timetable that counts down the weeks to go.

2. Work to a study plan.

Set up sessions of work spread through the weeks ahead. Make sure each session has a focus and a clear purpose. What will you study, when and why? Be realistic about what you can achieve in each session, and don't be afraid to adjust your plans as needed.

3. Make sure you know exactly when your exams are.

Get your exam dates from the SQA website and use the timetable builder tool to create your own exam schedule. You will also get a personalised timetable from your school, but this might not be until close to the exam period.

4. Make sure that you know the topics that make up each course.

Studying is easier if material is in manageable chunks – why not use the SQA topic headings or create your own from your class notes? Ask your teacher for help on this if you are not sure.

5. Break the chunks up into even smaller bits.

The small chunks should be easier to cope with. Remember that they fit together to make larger ideas. Even the process of chunking down will help!

6. Ask yourself these key questions for each course:

- Are all topics compulsory or are there choices?
- Which topics seem to come up time and time again?
- Which topics are your strongest and which are your weakest?

Use your answers to these questions to work out how much time you will need to spend revising each topic.

7. Make sure you know what to expect in the exam.

The subject-specific introduction to this book will help with this. Make sure you can answer these questions:

- How is the paper structured?
- How much time is there for each part of the exam?
- What types of question are involved? These will vary depending on the subject so read the subject-specific section carefully.

8. Past papers are a *vital revision tool!*

Use past papers to support your revision wherever possible. This book contains the answers and mark schemes too – refer to these carefully when checking your work. Using the mark scheme is useful; even if you don't manage to get all the marks available first time when you first practise, it helps you identify how to extend and develop your answers to get more marks next time – and of course, in the real exam.

9. Use study methods that work well for you.

People study and learn in different ways. Reading and looking at diagrams suits some students. Others prefer to listen and hear material – what about reading out loud or getting a friend or family member to do this for you? You could also record and play back material.

10. There are three tried and tested ways to make material stick in your long-term memory:

- Practising – e.g. rehearsal, repeating
- Organising – e.g. making drawings, lists, diagrams, tables, memory aids
- Elaborating – e.g. incorporating the material into a story or an imagined journey

11. Learn actively.

Most people prefer to learn actively – for example, making notes, highlighting, redrawing and redrafting, making up memory aids, or writing past paper answers. A good way to stay engaged and inspired is to mix and match these methods – find the combination that best suits you. This is likely to vary depending on the topic or subject.

12. Be an expert.

Be sure to have a few areas in which you feel you are an expert. This often works because at least some of them will come up, which can boost confidence.

13. Try some visual methods.

Use symbols, diagrams, charts, flashcards, post-it notes etc. Don't forget – the brain takes in chunked images more easily than loads of text.

14. Remember – practice makes perfect.

Work on difficult areas again and again. Look and read – then test yourself. You cannot do this too much.

15. Try past papers against the clock.

Practise writing answers in a set time. This is a good habit from the start but is especially important when you get closer to exam time.

16. Collaborate with friends.

Test each other and talk about the material – this can really help. Two brains are better than one! It is amazing how talking about a problem can help you solve it.

17. Know your weaknesses.

Ask your teacher for help to identify what you don't know. Try to do this as early as possible. If you are having trouble, it is probably with a difficult topic, so your teacher will already be aware of this – most students will find it tough.

18. Have your materials organised and ready.

Know what is needed for each exam:

- Do you need a calculator or a ruler?
- Should you have pencils as well as pens?
- Will you need water or paper tissues?

19. Make full use of school resources.

Find out what support is on offer:

- Are there study classes available?
- When is the library open?
- When is the best time to ask for extra help?
- Can you borrow textbooks, study guides, past papers, etc.?
- Is school open for Easter revision?

20. Keep fit and healthy!

Try to stick to a routine as much as possible, including with sleep. If you are tired, sluggish or dehydrated, it is difficult to see how concentration is even possible. Combine study with relaxation, drink plenty of water, eat sensibly, and get fresh air and exercise – all these things will help more than you could imagine. Good luck!

HIGHER

2017

National Qualifications 2017

X713/76/02

Chemistry
Section 1 — Questions

MONDAY, 8 MAY

9:00 AM — 11:30 AM

Instructions for the completion of Section 1 are given on *Page two* of your question and answer booklet X713/76/01.

Record your answers on the answer grid on *Page three* of your question and answer booklet.

You may refer to the Chemistry Data Booklet for Higher and Advanced Higher.

Before leaving the examination room you must give your question and answer booklet to the Invigilator; if you do not, you may lose all the marks for this paper.

SECTION 1 — 20 marks
Attempt ALL questions

1. Which of the following bonds is the **least** polar?

    A   C — I

    B   C — F

    C   C — Cl

    D   C — Br

2. Which of the following compounds would be the **most water** soluble?

A

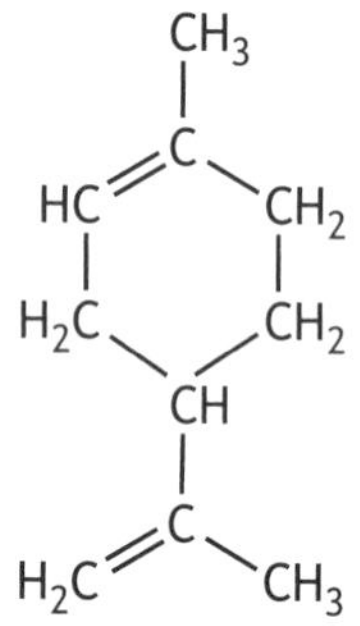

B

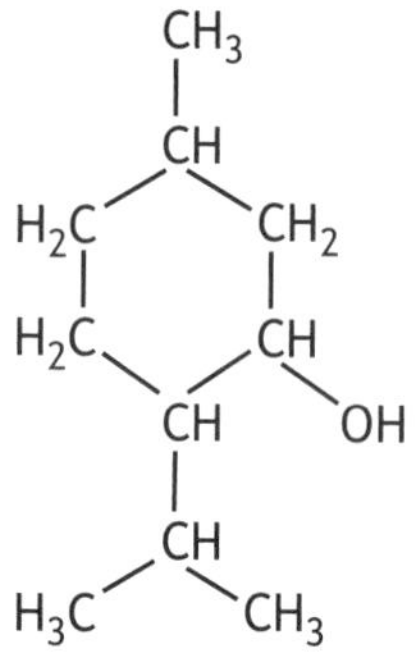

C

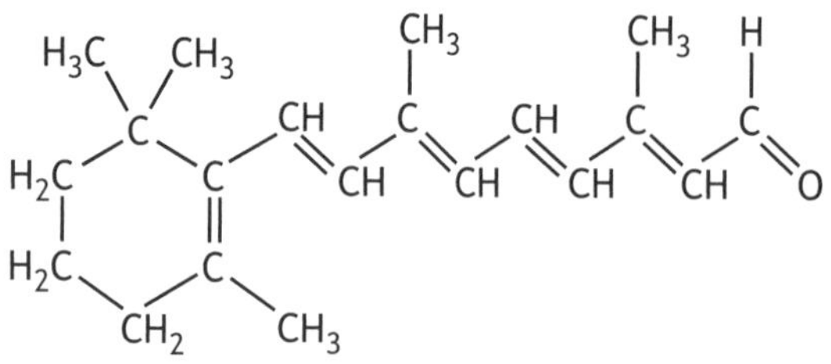

D

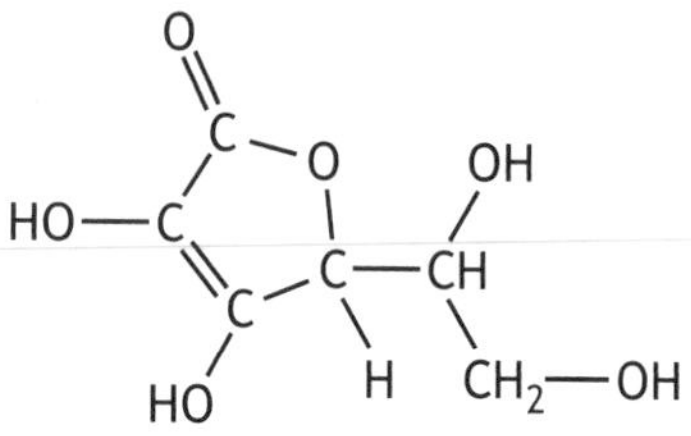

3. Which of the following atoms has the greatest attraction for bonding electrons?

    A   Sulfur

    B   Silicon

    C   Nitrogen

    D   Hydrogen

4. Which type of structure is found in phosphorus?

    A   Covalent network

    B   Covalent molecular

    C   Monatomic

    D   Metallic lattice

5. The polarity of molecules can be investigated using a charged rod. The charged rod will attract a stream of polar liquid flowing from a burette.

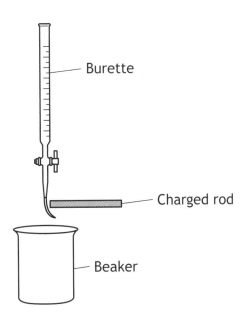

    Which of the following liquids would **not** be attracted?

    A   Water

    B   Propanone

    C   Propanol

    D   Hexane

[Turn over

6. $xP_2H_4 + yO_2 \rightarrow P_4O_{10} + zH_2O$

The equation is balanced when

A $x = 1, y = 5, z = 4$

B $x = 4, y = 6, z = 2$

C $x = 2, y = 7, z = 4$

D $x = 2, y = 5, z = 2$

7. What is the systematic name for the compound below?

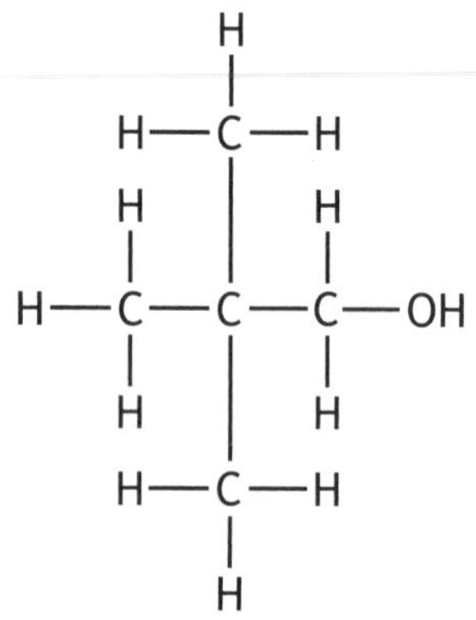

A 2,2,2-trimethylethanol

B 2,2-dimethylpropan-1-ol

C 2,2-dimethylpropan-3-ol

D 2,2-dimethylpentan-1-ol

8. Which of the following fatty acids is the most unsaturated?

A $C_{15}H_{29}COOH$

B $C_{15}H_{31}COOH$

C $C_{17}H_{31}COOH$

D $C_{17}H_{35}COOH$

9. Which of the following is **not** a step in a free radical chain reaction?

    A   Activation

    B   Initiation

    C   Propagation

    D   Termination

10. Which of the following is an isomer of ethyl propanoate ($CH_3CH_2COOCH_2CH_3$)?

    A   Methyl propanoate

    B   Pentan-2-one

    C   Pentanoic acid

    D   Pentane-1,2-diol

11. Essential oils are

    A   non-water soluble, non-volatile compounds

    B   non-water soluble, volatile compounds

    C   water soluble, non-volatile compounds

    D   water soluble, volatile compounds.

12. The enthalpy of combustion of a hydrocarbon is the enthalpy change when

    A   one mole of a hydrocarbon burns to give one mole of water

    B   one mole of a hydrocarbon burns to give one mole of carbon dioxide

    C   one mole of a hydrocarbon burns completely in oxygen

    D   one mole of a hydrocarbon burns in one mole of oxygen.

13. Which of the following is the strongest reducing agent?

    A   Fluorine

    B   Lithium

    C   Calcium

    D   Iodine

[Turn over

14.

$$TiCl_4 \quad + \quad 2Mg \quad \rightarrow \quad 2MgCl_2 \quad + \quad Ti$$

| mass of one mole = 189·9 g | mass of one mole = 24·3 g | mass of one mole = 95·3 g | mass of one mole = 47·9 g |

The atom economy for the production of titanium in the above equation is equal to

A $\dfrac{47 \cdot 9}{189 \cdot 9 + 24 \cdot 3} \times 100$

B $\dfrac{47 \cdot 9}{189 \cdot 9 + (2 \times 24 \cdot 3)} \times 100$

C $\dfrac{95 \cdot 3 + 47 \cdot 9}{189 \cdot 9 + 24 \cdot 3} \times 100$

D $\dfrac{(2 \times 47 \cdot 9)}{189 \cdot 9 + 24 \cdot 3} \times 100$

15. The vitamin C content of a carton of orange juice was determined by four students. Each student carried out the experiment three times.

	Experiment 1 (mg/100 cm^3)	Experiment 2 (mg/100 cm^3)	Experiment 3 (mg/100 cm^3)
Student A	30·0	29·0	28·0
Student B	26·4	26·6	26·8
Student C	26·9	27·0	26·9
Student D	26·9	26·5	26·9

The most reproducible results were obtained by

A Student A

B Student B

C Student C

D Student D.

16. Cyanohydrin compounds can be made from carbonyl compounds by reacting the carbonyl compound with hydrogen cyanide (HCN).

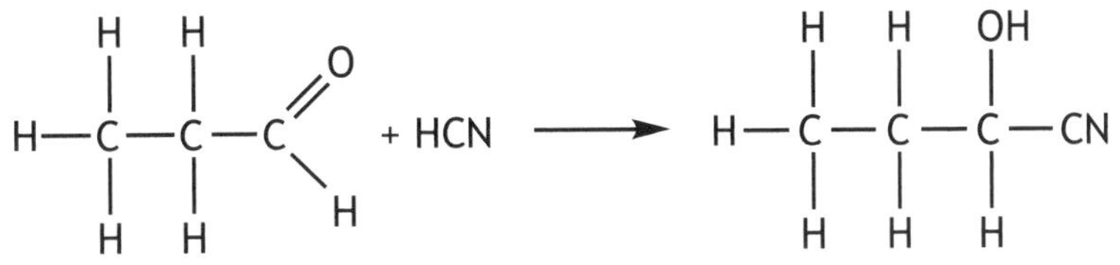

Which carbonyl compound would react with hydrogen cyanide (HCN) to form the following compound?

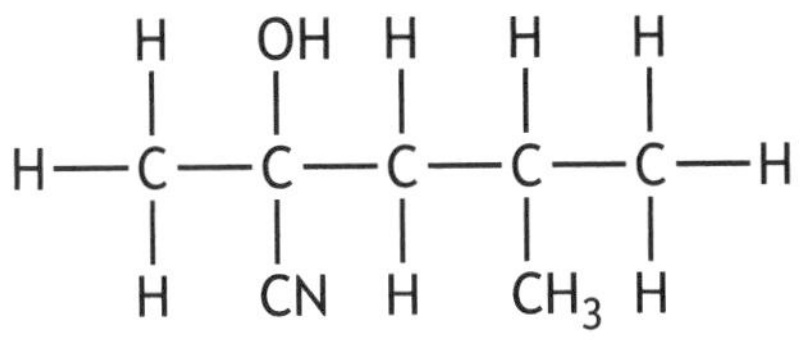

A

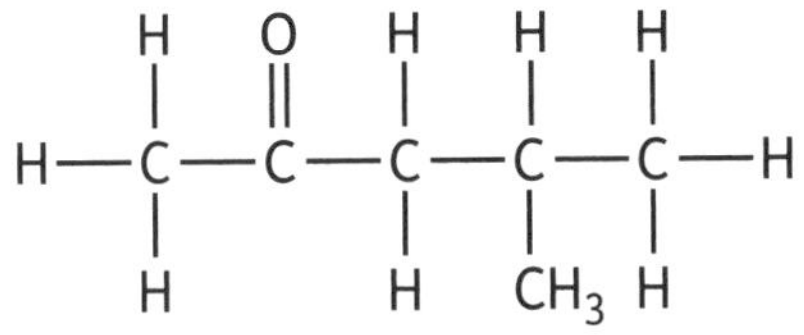

B

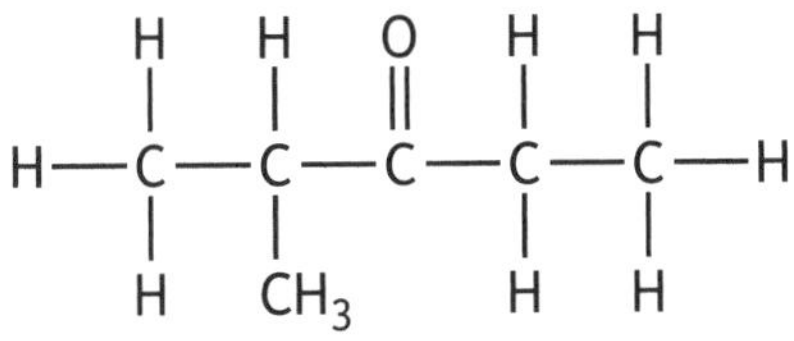

C

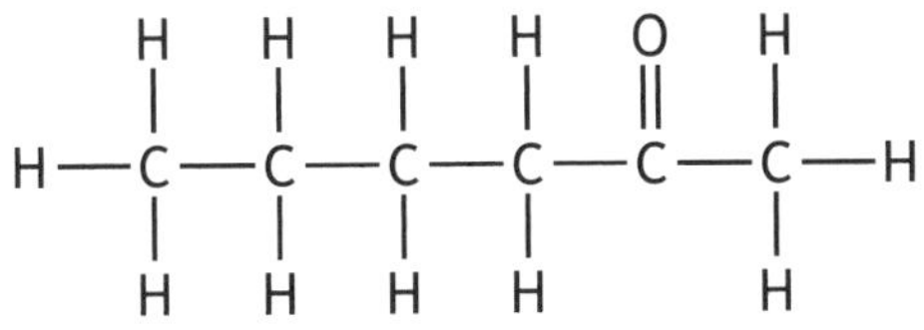

D

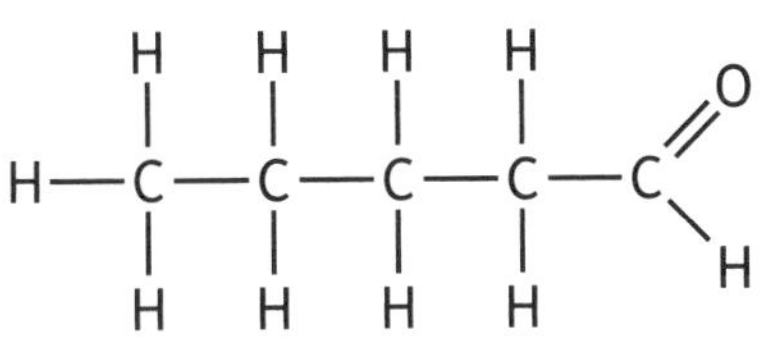

[Turn over

17. Chemical reactions are in a state of dynamic equilibrium only when

    A   the reaction involves no enthalpy change

    B   the concentrations of reactants and products are equal

    C   the activation energies of the forward and backward reactions are equal

    D   the rate of the forward reaction equals that of the backward reaction.

18. Bromine and hydrogen react together to form hydrogen bromide.

$$H_2(g) \ + \ Br_2(g) \ \longrightarrow \ 2HBr(g)$$

Bonds broken	Bonds made
H—H	$2 \times$ H—Br
Br—Br	

Bond	Bond enthalpy (kJ mol^{-1})
H—H	436
Br—Br	194
H—Br	366

The enthalpy change for this reaction, in kJ mol^{-1}, is

    A   −102

    B   +102

    C   −264

    D   +264.

19. Which of the following is a structural formula for glycerol?

A
$$CH_2OH$$
$$|$$
$$CH_2$$
$$|$$
$$CH_2OH$$

B
$$CH_2OH$$
$$|$$
$$CH_2OH$$

C
$$CH_2OH$$
$$|$$
$$CHOH$$
$$|$$
$$CH_2COOH$$

D
$$CH_2OH$$
$$|$$
$$CHOH$$
$$|$$
$$CH_2OH$$

20. Which line in the table best describes the effect of adding a catalyst to the following reaction?

$$4NH_3(g) + 5O_2(g) \rightleftharpoons 4NO(g) + 6H_2O(g) \qquad \Delta H = -ve$$

	Position of equilibrium	Rate of forward reaction
A	unchanged	unchanged
B	unchanged	increased
C	moves to right	unchanged
D	moves to right	increased

[END OF SECTION 1. NOW ATTEMPT THE QUESTIONS IN SECTION 2 OF YOUR QUESTION AND ANSWER BOOKLET.]

[BLANK PAGE]

DO NOT WRITE ON THIS PAGE

H

National Qualifications 2017

Mark

X713/76/01

Chemistry
Section 1 — Answer Grid and Section 2

MONDAY, 8 MAY

9:00 AM — 11:30 AM

Fill in these boxes and read what is printed below.

Full name of centre

Town

Forename(s)

Surname

Number of seat

Date of birth

Day   Month   Year   Scottish candidate number

Total marks — 100

SECTION 1 — 20 marks

Attempt ALL questions.

Instructions for the completion of Section 1 are given on *Page two*.

SECTION 2 — 80 marks

Attempt ALL questions.

You may refer to the Chemistry Data Booklet for Higher and Advanced Higher.

Write your answers clearly in the spaces provided in this booklet. Additional space for answers and rough work is provided at the end of this booklet. If you use this space you must clearly identify the question number you are attempting. Any rough work must be written in this booklet. You should score through your rough work when you have written your final copy.

Use **blue** or **black** ink.

Before leaving the examination room you must give this booklet to the Invigilator; if you do not, you may lose all the marks for this paper.

SECTION 1 — 20 marks

The questions for Section 1 are contained in the question paper X713/76/02.

Read these and record your answers on the answer grid on *Page three* opposite.

Use **blue** or **black** ink. Do NOT use gel pens or pencil.

1. The answer to each question is **either** A, B, C or D. Decide what your answer is, then fill in the appropriate bubble (see sample question below).

2. There is **only one correct** answer to each question.

3. Any rough working should be done on the additional space for answers and rough work at the end of this booklet.

Sample Question

To show that the ink in a ball-pen consists of a mixture of dyes, the method of separation would be:

    A   fractional distillation

    B   chromatography

    C   fractional crystallisation

    D   filtration.

The correct answer is **B** — chromatography. The answer **B** bubble has been clearly filled in (see below).

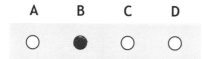

Changing an answer

If you decide to change your answer, cancel your first answer by putting a cross through it (see below) and fill in the answer you want. The answer below has been changed to **D**.

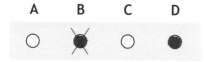

If you then decide to change back to an answer you have already scored out, put a tick (✓) to the **right** of the answer you want, as shown below:

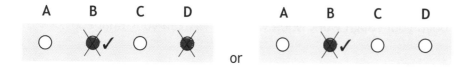

or

SECTION 1 — Answer Grid

	A	B	C	D
1	○	○	○	○
2	○	○	○	○
3	○	○	○	○
4	○	○	○	○
5	○	○	○	○
6	○	○	○	○
7	○	○	○	○
8	○	○	○	○
9	○	○	○	○
10	○	○	○	○
11	○	○	○	○
12	○	○	○	○
13	○	○	○	○
14	○	○	○	○
15	○	○	○	○
16	○	○	○	○
17	○	○	○	○
18	○	○	○	○
19	○	○	○	○
20	○	○	○	○

[Turn over

[BLANK PAGE]

DO NOT WRITE ON THIS PAGE

[Turn over for next question

DO NOT WRITE ON THIS PAGE

MARKS | DO NOT WRITE IN THIS MARGIN

SECTION 2 — 80 marks

Attempt ALL questions

1. The elements sodium to argon make up the third period of the Periodic Table.

Na	Mg	Al	Si	P	S	Cl	Ar

(a) Name the element from the third period that exists as a covalent network.

1

(b) Ionisation energy changes across the period.

(i) Explain why the first ionisation energy increases across the period.

1

(ii) Write an equation, including state symbols, for the **second** ionisation energy of magnesium.

1

(iii) The table shows the values for the first four ionisation energies of aluminium.

Ionisation energies (kJ mol^{-1})			
First	Second	Third	Fourth
578	1817	2745	11 577

Explain why there is a large difference between the third and fourth ionisation energies.

1

Page six

MARKS | DO NOT WRITE IN THIS MARGIN

1. **(continued)**

(c) The boiling point of chlorine is much higher than that of argon.

Explain **fully**, in terms of structure and the type of van der Waals forces present, why the boiling point of chlorine is higher than that of argon.   **3**

MARKS | DO NOT WRITE IN THIS MARGIN

2. Reactions involving iodine are commonly used to investigate rates of reaction.

  (a) One reaction involves hydrogen and iodine reacting together to form hydrogen iodide.

$$H_2(g) \quad + \quad I_2(g) \quad \rightleftharpoons \quad 2HI(g)$$

    (i) This reaction is thought to occur by initially breaking bonds in one of the reactants.

      Explain, using bond enthalpies, which bond is more likely to break first during this reaction.

      1

    (ii) The graph shows the distribution of kinetic energies of reactant molecules in the gas mixture at 300 °C.

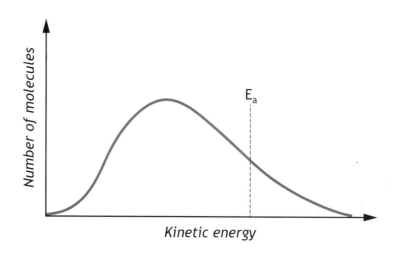

      Add a second curve to the graph to show the distribution of kinetic energies at 400 °C.

      1

      (An additional graph, if required, can be found on *Page thirty-five*)

MARKS | DO NOT WRITE IN THIS MARGIN

2. (a) (continued)

(iii) The reaction to produce hydrogen iodide is exothermic.

$$H_2(g) \ + \ I_2(g) \ \rightleftharpoons \ 2HI(g)$$

(A) State the effect of increasing temperature on the position of equilibrium.

1

(B) State why changing the pressure has no effect on this equilibrium reaction.

1

MARKS | DO NOT WRITE IN THIS MARGIN

2. (a) (continued)

(iv) The potential energy diagram for the reaction between hydrogen and iodine is shown.

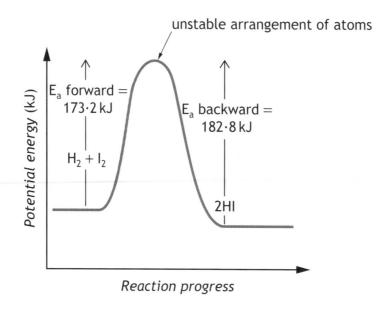

(A) State the term for the unstable arrangement of atoms. **1**

(B) Calculate the enthalpy change, in kJ, for the forward reaction. **1**

(C) Platinum can be used as a catalyst for this reaction.

State the effect that platinum would have on the activation energy for the reaction. **1**

MARKS | DO NOT WRITE IN THIS MARGIN

2. (continued)

(b) The reaction between iodide ions, I^-(aq), and persulfate ions, $S_2O_8^{2-}$(aq), is used to investigate the effect of changing concentration on rate of reaction. The relative rate of the reaction is determined by mixing the reactants in a beaker and recording the time taken for the mixture to change colour.

The results of the investigation are shown in the table.

Experiment	Concentration of I^-(aq) (mol l^{-1})	Concentration of $S_2O_8^{2-}$(aq) (mol l^{-1})	Time (s)	Relative rate (s^{-1})
1	0·04	0·05	241	0·00415
2	0·06	0·05	180	0·00556
3	0·08	0·05		0·00819
4	0·1	0·05	103	0·00971

(i) The instructions state that a dry beaker must be used for each experiment.

Suggest a reason why the beaker should be dry.   1

(ii) Calculate the time, in seconds, for the reaction in experiment 3.   1

(iii) Explain why decreasing the concentration of iodide ions lowers the reaction rate.   1

[Turn over

MARKS | DO NOT WRITE IN THIS MARGIN

3. The leaves of the rhubarb plant are considered poisonous because they contain high levels of oxalic acid.

Oxalic acid is a white, water-soluble solid. It is a dicarboxylic acid that has the structural formula shown.

Oxalic acid reacts with bases to form salts.

It can also be oxidised by strong oxidising agents to form carbon dioxide gas. The oxidation equation for oxalic acid is shown.

$$H_2C_2O_4 \longrightarrow 2CO_2 + 2e^- + 2H^+$$

Using your knowledge of chemistry, comment on how the mass of oxalic acid in a rhubarb leaf could be determined.

3

MARKS | DO NOT WRITE IN THIS MARGIN

4. Pentyl butanoate is responsible for some of the flavour in apricots and strawberries.

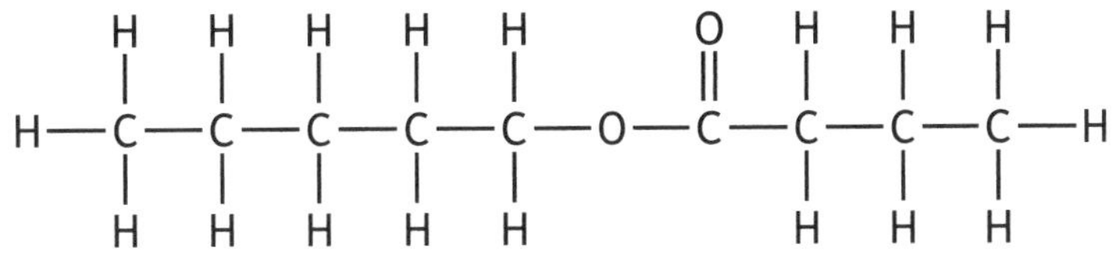

(a) Hydrolysis of pentyl butanoate using sodium hydroxide produces an alcohol and the salt of the carboxylic acid.

(i) Name the alcohol that would be formed when pentyl butanoate is hydrolysed. **1**

(ii) Draw a structural formula for the sodium salt of the carboxylic acid that would be formed. **1**

(b) Fats and oils belong to the same class of compounds as pentyl butanoate.

(i) Name this class of compounds. **1**

(ii) When a fat is hydrolysed using sodium hydroxide, sodium salts of fatty acids are produced.

State a use for sodium salts of fatty acids. **1**

MARKS | DO NOT WRITE IN THIS MARGIN

4. (b) (continued)

(iii) Hydrolysis of fats using hydrochloric acid produces fatty acids. Stearic acid is a fatty acid that can be made from hydrolysis of beef fat. It is a fuel sometimes found in fireworks.

During combustion, stearic acid ($C_{17}H_{35}COOH$) produces 623 kJ of energy **per mole of CO_2 produced.**

$$C_{17}H_{35}COOH \ + \ 26O_2 \ \longrightarrow \ 18CO_2 \ + \ 18H_2O$$

mass of
one mole
$= 284\,g$

Calculate the energy released, in kJ, by combustion of 10 grams of stearic acid. 2

5. Sulfur dioxide is a colourless, toxic gas that is soluble in water and more dense than air.

    (a) One laboratory method for preparation of sulfur dioxide gas involves adding dilute hydrochloric acid to solid sodium sulfite. The sulfur dioxide gas produced is dried by bubbling the gas through concentrated sulfuric acid. The sulfur dioxide gas can then be collected.

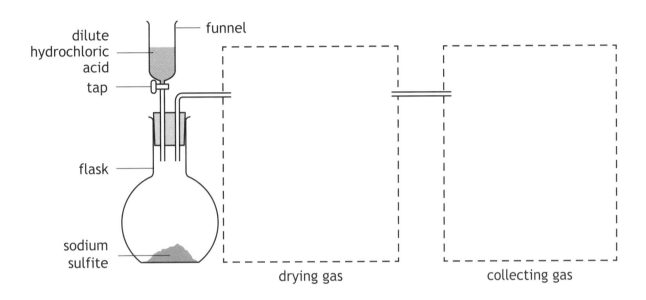

MARKS | DO NOT WRITE IN THIS MARGIN

    (i) Complete the diagram by drawing:

        in the first box, apparatus suitable for drying the sulfur dioxide gas;

        in the second box, apparatus suitable for collecting the gas.   2

        (An additional diagram, if required, can be found on *Page thirty-five*)

MARKS | DO NOT WRITE IN THIS MARGIN

5. (a) (continued)

(ii) 0·40 g of sodium sulfite, Na_2SO_3, is reacted with 50 cm³ of dilute hydrochloric acid, concentration 1·0 mol l⁻¹.

$$Na_2SO_3(s) + 2HCl(aq) \rightarrow H_2O(\ell) + 2NaCl(aq) + SO_2(g)$$

mass of
one mole
= 126·1 g

Show, by calculation, that sodium sulfite is the limiting reactant.   2

(b) Another reaction that produces sulfur dioxide gas involves combustion of carbon disulfide in the reaction shown.

$$CS_2(\ell) + 3O_2(g) \rightarrow CO_2(g) + 2SO_2(g)$$

Calculate the enthalpy change, in kJ mol⁻¹, for this reaction using the following information.   2

C(s) +	$O_2(g)$	$\rightarrow$	$CO_2(g)$	$\Delta H = -393 \cdot 5\,kJ\,mol^{-1}$
S(s) +	$O_2(g)$	$\rightarrow$	$SO_2(g)$	$\Delta H = -296 \cdot 8\,kJ\,mol^{-1}$
C(s) +	2S(s)	$\rightarrow$	$CS_2(\ell)$	$\Delta H = +87 \cdot 9\,kJ\,mol^{-1}$

5.   (continued)

MARKS | DO NOT WRITE IN THIS MARGIN

(c)   The graph shows results for an experiment to determine the solubility of sulfur dioxide in water.

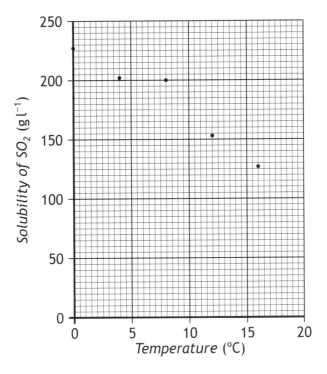

(i)   Determine the solubility of sulfur dioxide, in $g\,l^{-1}$, in water at 10°C.   1

(ii)   Information about sulfur dioxide and carbon dioxide is shown in the table.

	Shape of molecule	Electronegativity difference between elements	Solubility in water at 25 °C ($g\,l^{-1}$)
carbon dioxide	linear O=C=O	1·0	1·45
sulfur dioxide	bent S with O=S=O	1·0	94

Explain **fully** why carbon dioxide is much less soluble in water than sulfur dioxide is in water.   2

MARKS | DO NOT WRITE IN THIS MARGIN

6. A student was carrying out an investigation into alcohols, aldehydes and ketones.

(a) The student was given three alcohols labelled as **A**, **B** and **C**. These alcohols were all isomers with the formula C_4H_9OH.

(i) Draw a structural formula for the secondary alcohol with the formula C_4H_9OH.

1

(ii) The student set up the following experiment.

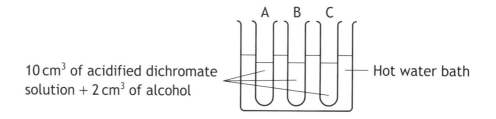

$10\,cm^3$ of acidified dichromate solution $+ 2\,cm^3$ of alcohol

Hot water bath

Alcohol	Observation
A	Colour change
B	No change
C	Colour change

(A) Suggest why a water bath is an appropriate method of heating the reaction mixture.

1

(B) Describe the colour change that would have been observed with alcohols **A** and **C**.

1

(C) Alcohol **B** is not oxidised.

State the **type** of alcohol which cannot be oxidised by acidified dichromate solution.

1

MARKS | DO NOT WRITE IN THIS MARGIN

6. **(a)** **(continued)**

(iii) The student set up a second experiment with alcohol **A**.

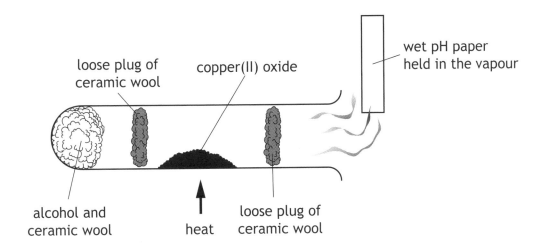

loose plug of ceramic wool   copper(II) oxide   wet pH paper held in the vapour

alcohol and ceramic wool   heat   loose plug of ceramic wool

Hot copper(II) oxide is an oxidising agent.

(A) When alcohol **A** (C_4H_9OH) is oxidised the product turns the pH paper red.

Suggest a name for the product.   1

(B) Complete the ion-electron equation for the oxidation reaction.   1

$$C_4H_9OH \longrightarrow C_4H_8O_2$$

MARKS | DO NOT WRITE IN THIS MARGIN

6.   (continued)

(b)   The student found the following information about the boiling points of some aldehydes.

Aldehyde	Molecular formula	Boiling point (°C)
	$C_5H_{10}O$	102
	$C_6H_{12}O$	130
	$C_7H_{14}O$	153
	$C_5H_{10}O$	95
	$C_5H_{10}O$	75
	$C_6H_{12}O$	119
	$C_6H_{12}O$	111

(i)   Name the aldehyde that has a boiling point of 119 °C.   1

(ii) Predict the boiling point, in °C, of the following molecule.   1

MARKS | DO NOT WRITE IN THIS MARGIN

6. (b) (continued)

(iii) Using information from the table, describe one way in which differences in structure affect the boiling point of **isomeric** aldehydes.

1

(iv) State what would be observed when an aldehyde is gently heated with Tollens' reagent.

1

(c) Ketones contain a carbonyl group.

Name the type of intermolecular interaction between ketone molecules.

1

MARKS | DO NOT WRITE IN THIS MARGIN

7. Some people take iron tablets as a dietary supplement. Iron tablets may contain iron(II) sulfate.

(a) A student was investigating the iron(II) content of iron tablets. A work card gave the following instructions for preparing an iron tablet solution.

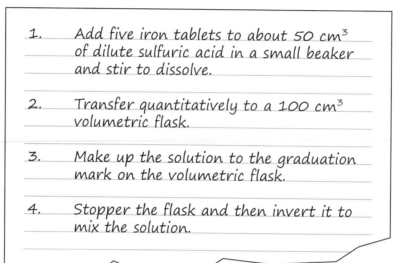

1. Add five iron tablets to about 50 cm³ of dilute sulfuric acid in a small beaker and stir to dissolve.

2. Transfer quantitatively to a 100 cm³ volumetric flask.

3. Make up the solution to the graduation mark on the volumetric flask.

4. Stopper the flask and then invert it to mix the solution.

To 'transfer quantitatively' means that **all** of the iron tablet solution must be transferred into the volumetric flask.

Describe how this is carried out in practice. 1

(b) The concentration of iron(II) ions (Fe^{2+}) in this iron tablet solution can be determined by a redox titration with permanganate (MnO_4^-) solution.

$$5Fe^{2+}(aq) + 8H^+(aq) + MnO_4^-(aq) \rightarrow 5Fe^{3+}(aq) + Mn^{2+}(aq) + 4H_2O(\ell)$$

(i) Suggest why it is **not** necessary to add an indicator to this titration. 1

MARKS | DO NOT WRITE IN THIS MARGIN

7. (b) (continued)

(ii) Suggest why the titration must be carried out under acidic conditions.

1

(iii) Three 25·0 cm³ samples of the iron tablet solution were titrated with a standard solution of 0·020 mol l⁻¹ permanganate (MnO_4^-). The results are shown below.

Sample	Volume of permanganate (cm³)
1	14·9
2	14·5
3	14·6

(A) State why the volume of permanganate used in the calculation was taken to be 14·55 cm³, although this is not the average of the three titres in the table.

1

(B) Calculate the concentration, in mol l⁻¹, of iron(II) ions in the iron tablet solution.

3

$$5Fe^{2+}(aq) + 8H^+(aq) + MnO_4^-(aq) \rightarrow 5Fe^{3+}(aq) + Mn^{2+}(aq) + 4H_2O(\ell)$$

[Turn over

MARKS | DO NOT WRITE IN THIS MARGIN

7. **(b)** **(iii)** **(continued)**

    (C)   State what is meant by the term **standard solution**.

                      1

    (D)   Name an appropriate piece of apparatus which could be used to measure $25 \cdot 0 \, cm^3$ samples of iron tablet solution.

                      1

(c) In a different experiment, five iron tablets were found to contain 0·00126 moles of iron(II) ions.

Calculate the average mass, in **mg**, of iron present in **one** tablet.

                      1

(d) It is recommended an adult female takes in 14·8 mg of iron per day.

100 g of a breakfast cereal contains 12·0 mg of iron.

Calculate the percentage of the recommended daily amount of iron provided for an adult female by a 30 g serving.

                      2

8. Skin care products contain a mixture of polar covalent, non-polar covalent and ionic compounds. The compounds need to stay mixed within the product.

Skin care products also need to spread easily and remain on the skin for a period of time, as well as provide physical and chemical protection from the sun. In order to do this, skin care products contain a range of chemicals including water, fats and oils, antioxidants, minerals and sun block.

Using your knowledge of chemistry, explain the role of different chemicals in skin care products.

3

[BLANK PAGE]

DO NOT WRITE ON THIS PAGE

MARKS | DO NOT WRITE IN THIS MARGIN

9. Dishwasher tablets contain chemicals which remove dirt from dishes.

   (a) Dishwasher tablets include detergents. These molecules act like soaps to allow mixing of fat-soluble dirt and water.

      (i) During the cleaning process, the detergent molecules combine with fat-soluble dirt.

      A simplified diagram of a detergent molecule is shown.

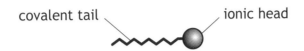

covalent tail   ionic head

      Complete the diagram below to show how detergent molecules combine with fat-soluble dirt.

1

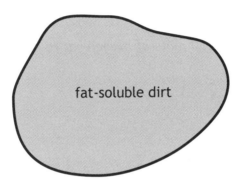

fat-soluble dirt

      (An additional diagram, if required, can be found on *Page thirty-six*)

      (ii) State the term used to describe the non-polar, hydrocarbon tail of a detergent molecule.

1

[Turn over

MARKS | DO NOT WRITE IN THIS MARGIN

9.   (continued)

(b) Dishwasher tablets produce the bleach hydrogen peroxide, H_2O_2. One action of this oxidising agent is to oxidise food.

(i) Suggest another action of the bleach produced by the dishwasher tablets.

1

(ii) Hydrogen peroxide decomposes to form water and oxygen.

$$2H_2O_2(\ell) \quad \rightarrow \quad 2H_2O(\ell) \quad + \quad O_2(g)$$

A dishwasher tablet produces 0·051 g of hydrogen peroxide (mass of one mole = 34 g).

Calculate the volume of oxygen that would be produced when 0·051 g of hydrogen peroxide decomposes.

Take the volume of 1 mole of oxygen gas to be 24 litres.

3

(c) Enzymes are commonly added to dishwasher tablets. These are used to break down proteins.

(i) The proteins are broken down into small, water-soluble molecules.

Name the small, water-soluble molecules made when proteins are broken down completely.

1

MARKS | DO NOT WRITE IN THIS MARGIN

9. (c) (continued)

(ii) The structure of a section of protein chain found in egg white is shown.

(A) Name the functional group circled. 1

(B) Draw a structural formula for **one** of the molecules that would be made when this section of egg white protein chain is completely broken down. 1

(iii) As part of the program in the dishwasher, the conditions in the dishwasher change so that the enzyme molecules no longer work because they change shape.

(A) State the term used to describe the change in shape of enzyme molecules. 1

(B) Suggest a change in conditions which would cause the enzyme molecules to change shape. 1

MARKS | DO NOT WRITE IN THIS MARGIN

9. **(continued)**

(d) A bleach activator is frequently added to dishwasher tablets to speed up the bleaching reaction. One common bleach activator is TAED.

TAED could be produced in a process which involves a number of stages.

(i) The first stage in producing TAED is shown below.

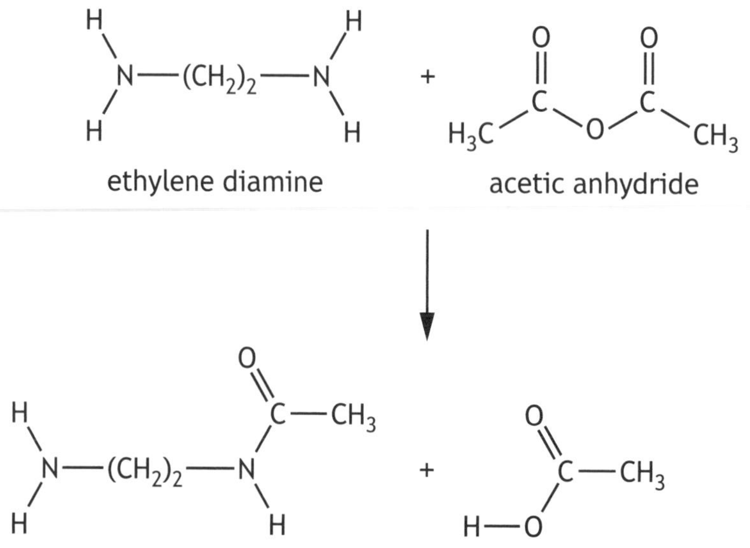

ethylene diamine   acetic anhydride

Suggest a name for this type of reaction.   1

MARKS | DO NOT WRITE IN THIS MARGIN

9.   (d)   (continued)

(ii)   The final stage in the process producing TAED is shown below.

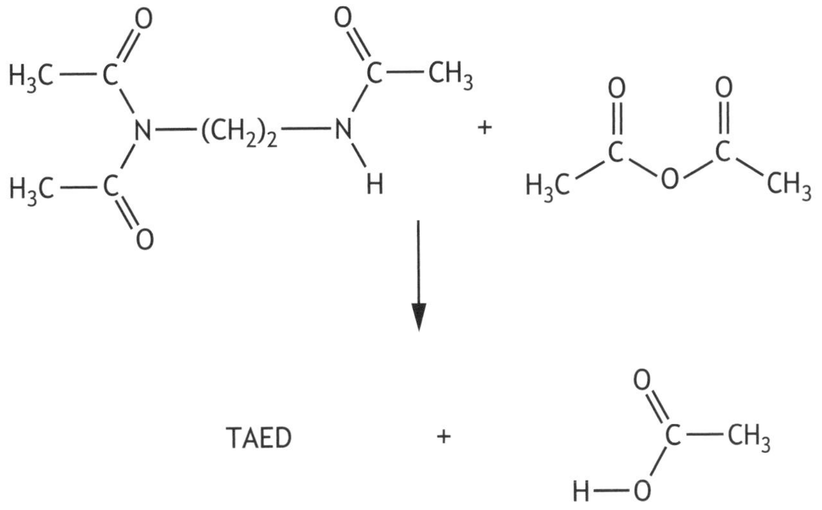

Draw a structural formula for TAED.   1

[Turn over

10. Essential oils from the lavender plant are used in aromatherapy.

   (a) Gas chromatography can be used to separate and identify the organic compounds in lavender oils.

Chromatogram 1 — Lavender oil **A**

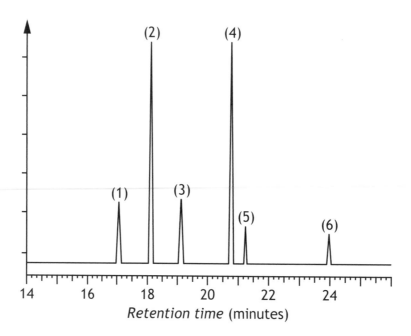

Peak	Component	Component peak area
1	1,8-cineole	7432
2	linalool	31 909
3	camphor	7518
4	linalyl acetate	27 504
5	geranyl acetate	3585
6	farnesene	1362

Total peak area   =   79 310

The relative concentration of each component can be calculated using the following formula.

$$\text{Relative concentration} = \frac{\text{Component peak area}}{\text{Total peak area}} \times 100 \ (\%)$$

    (i) Calculate the relative concentration of linalool in lavender oil **A**.   1

MARKS | DO NOT WRITE IN THIS MARGIN

10. **(a)** **(continued)**

(ii) Different varieties of lavender oils have different compositions.

Chromatogram 2 — Lavender oil **B**

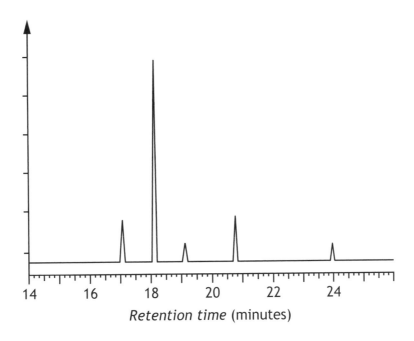

Retention time (minutes)

Identify the component found in lavender oil **A** that is missing from lavender oil **B**.   1

(b) A brand of mouthwash contains the component 1,8-cineole at a concentration of 0·92 mg per cm^3. The cost of 1 kg of 1,8-cineole is £59·10.

Calculate the cost, in pence, of 1,8-cineole that is present in a 500 cm^3 bottle of this brand of mouthwash.   2

MARKS | DO NOT WRITE IN THIS MARGIN

10. (continued)

(c) The component molecules found in lavender oils are terpenes or terpenoids.

(i) A chiral carbon is a carbon atom attached to **four** different atoms or groups of atoms.

An example is shown below.

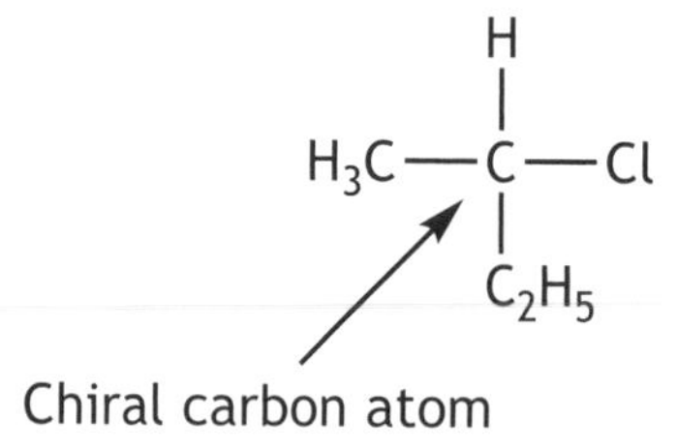

Chiral carbon atom

A molecule of the terpenoid linalool has a chiral carbon. Linalool has the following structure.

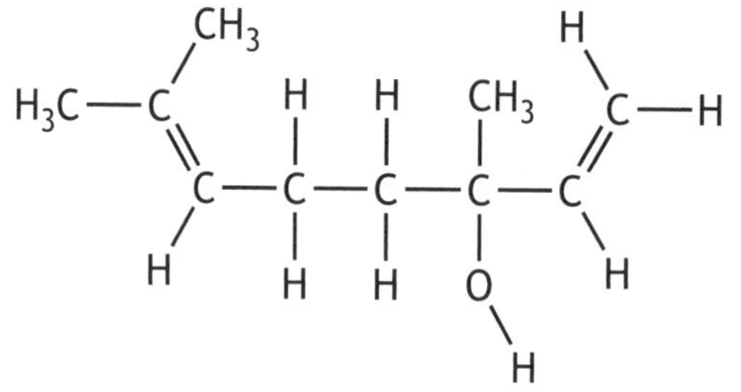

Circle the chiral carbon atom in the linalool structure.   1

(An additional diagram, if required, can be found on *Page thirty-six*)

(ii) Farnesene is a terpene consisting of **three** isoprene units (2-methylbuta-1,3-diene) joined together.

Write the molecular formula of farnesene.   1

[END OF QUESTION PAPER]

ADDITIONAL SPACE FOR ANSWERS AND ROUGH WORK

ADDITIONAL DIAGRAM FOR USE IN QUESTION 2 (a) (ii)

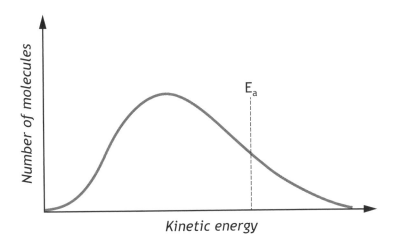

ADDITIONAL DIAGRAM FOR USE IN QUESTION 5 (a) (i)

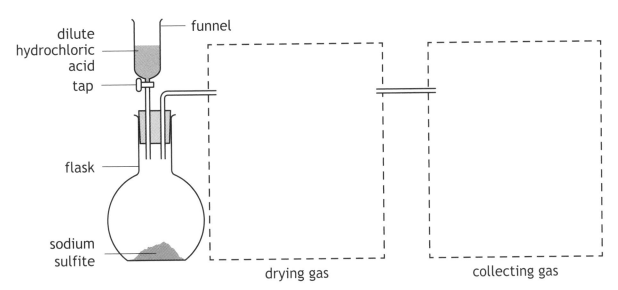

ADDITIONAL SPACE FOR ANSWERS AND ROUGH WORK

ADDITIONAL DIAGRAM FOR USE IN QUESTION 9 (a) (i)

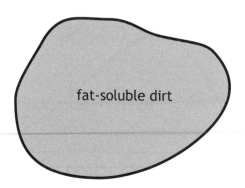

fat-soluble dirt

ADDITIONAL DIAGRAM FOR USE IN QUESTION 10 (c) (i)

ADDITIONAL SPACE FOR ANSWERS AND ROUGH WORK

ADDITIONAL SPACE FOR ANSWERS AND ROUGH WORK

HIGHER

2018

National Qualifications 2018

X713/76/02

Chemistry
Section 1 — Questions

MONDAY, 21 MAY

9:00 AM – 11:30 AM

Instructions for the completion of Section 1 are given on *Page two* of your question and answer booklet X713/76/01.

Record your answers on the answer grid on *Page three* of your question and answer booklet.

You may refer to the Chemistry Data Booklet for Higher and Advanced Higher.

Before leaving the examination room you must give your question and answer booklet to the Invigilator; if you do not, you may lose all the marks for this paper.

SECTION 1 — 20 marks

Attempt ALL questions

1. The potential energy diagram below refers to the reversible reaction involving reactants **R** and products **P**.

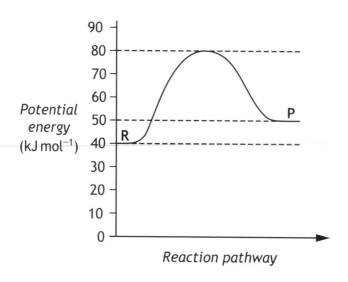

What is the enthalpy change, in $kJ\,mol^{-1}$, for the **reverse** reaction?

A   −40

B   −10

C   +10

D   +30

2. The relative rate of a reaction which reached completion in 1 minute 40 seconds is

A $0.010\,s^{-1}$

B $0.714\,s^{-1}$

C $0.010\,min^{-1}$

D $0.714\,min^{-1}$.

3.

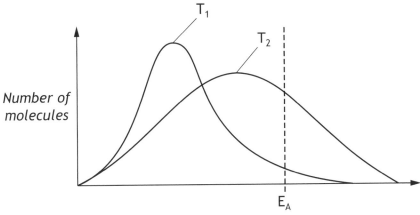

Kinetic energy of molecules

Which of the following is the correct interpretation of the above energy distribution diagram for a reaction as the temperature **decreases** from T_2 to T_1?

	Activation energy (E_A)	Number of successful collisions
A	remains the same	increases
B	decreases	decreases
C	decreases	increases
D	remains the same	decreases

4. The table shows the first three ionisation energies of aluminium.

Ionisation energy (kJ mol^{-1})		
First	Second	Third
578	1817	2745

Using this information, what is the enthalpy change, in kJ mol^{-1}, for the following reaction?

$$Al^+(g) \rightarrow Al^{3+}(g) + 2e^-$$

A   1817

B   2395

C   4562

D   5140

[Turn over

5. An element contains covalent bonding and London dispersion forces.

The element could be

A boron

B neon

C sodium

D sulfur.

6. Erythrose is a chemical that is known to kill cancer cells.

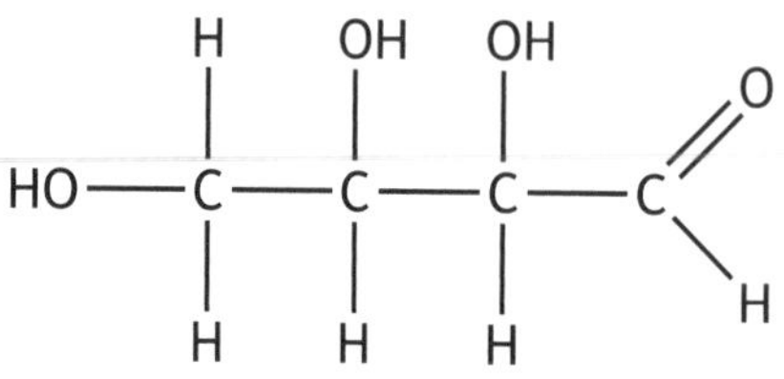

erythrose

The two functional groups present in erythrose are

A carboxyl and ester

B carbonyl and ester

C carbonyl and hydroxyl

D carboxyl and hydroxyl.

7.

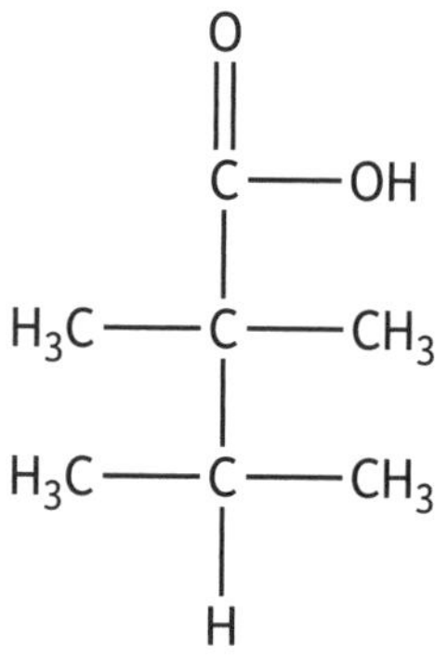

The name of the above compound is

A 2,2,3-trimethylbutanoic acid

B 2,3,3-trimethylbutanoic acid

C 1,1,2,2-tetramethylpropanoic acid

D 2,2,3,3-tetramethylpropanoic acid.

8. Which of the following is an isomer of pentan-3-ol?

   A $CH_3CH_2CH(OH)CH_2CH_3$

   B $CH_3CHCHCH_2CH_2OH$

   C $CH_3CHCHCH(OH)CH_3$

   D $CH_3CH(CH_3)CH_2CH_2OH$

9. Oxidation of 4-methylpentan-2-ol to the corresponding ketone results in the alcohol

   A   losing 2 g per mole

   B   gaining 2 g per mole

   C   losing 16 g per mole

   D   gaining 16 g per mole.

10. Essential amino acids are defined as the amino acids which

   A   are necessary for building proteins

   B   humans must acquire through their diet

   C   plants cannot synthesise for themselves

   D   are produced when any protein is hydrolysed.

11. A mixture of carbon monoxide and hydrogen can be converted into water and a mixture of hydrocarbons.

   $$n\, CO \ + \ (2n + 1)\, H_2 \ \rightarrow \ n\, H_2O \ + \ \text{hydrocarbons}$$

   What is the general formula for the hydrocarbons produced?

   A C_nH_{2n-2}

   B C_nH_{2n}

   C C_nH_{2n+1}

   D C_nH_{2n+2}

12. A mixture of sodium chloride and sodium sulfate is known to contain 0·6 mol of chloride ions and 0·2 mol of sulfate ions.

   How many moles of sodium ions are present?

   A   0·4

   B   0·5

   C   0·8

   D   1·0

13. Under the same conditions of temperature and pressure, which of the following gases would occupy the largest volume?

    A   0·20 g of hydrogen

    B   0·44 g of carbon dioxide

    C   0·60 g of neon

    D   0·80 g of argon

14. $3CuO + 2NH_3 \rightarrow 3Cu + N_2 + 3H_2O$

    What volume of gas, in cm^3, would be obtained by reaction between $100\,cm^3$ of ammonia gas and excess copper(II) oxide?

    All volumes are measured at atmospheric pressure and $20\,°C$.

    A   50

    B   100

    C   200

    D   400

15. $Cl_2(g) + H_2O(\ell) \rightleftharpoons Cl^-(aq) + ClO^-(aq) + 2H^+(aq)$

    The addition of which of the following substances would move the above equilibrium to the right?

    A   Hydrogen

    B   Hydrogen chloride

    C   Sodium chloride

    D   Sodium hydroxide

16. When 3·6 g of butanal (mass of one mole = 72 g) was burned, 124 kJ of energy was released.

    What is the enthalpy of combustion of butanal, in $kJ\,mol^{-1}$?

    A   −6·2

    B   +6·2

    C   −2480

    D   +2480

17. Consider the reaction pathways shown below.

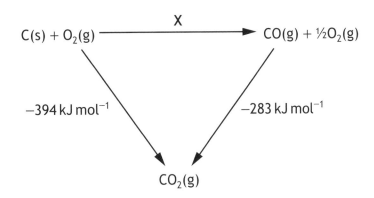

According to Hess's Law, the enthalpy change, in $kJ\,mol^{-1}$, for reaction X is

A   +111

B   −111

C   −677

D   +677.

18. $SO_3^{2-}(aq) + H_2O(\ell) \rightarrow SO_4^{2-}(aq) + 2H^+(aq) + 2e^-$

Which of the following ions could be used to oxidise sulfite ions to sulfate ions?

A $Cr^{3+}(aq)$

B $Al^{3+}(aq)$

C $Fe^{3+}(aq)$

D $Sn^{4+}(aq)$

19. During a redox reaction nitrate ions, NO_3^-, are converted to nitrogen monoxide, NO.

$$NO_3^- \rightarrow NO$$

Which line in the table correctly completes the ion-electron equation?

	Reactants	Products
A	$6H^+ + 5e^-$	$3H_2O$
B	$4H^+ + 3e^-$	$2H_2O$
C	$6H^+$	$3H_2O + 5e^-$
D	$4H^+$	$2H_2O + 3e^-$

20. $ICl(\ell) + Cl_2(g) \rightleftharpoons ICl_3(s)$ $\Delta H = -106\,kJ\,mol^{-1}$

Which line in the table identifies correctly the changes that will cause the greatest increase in the proportion of solid in the above equilibrium mixture?

	Temperature	Pressure
A	decrease	decrease
B	decrease	increase
C	increase	decrease
D	increase	increase

[END OF SECTION 1. NOW ATTEMPT THE QUESTIONS IN SECTION 2 OF YOUR QUESTION AND ANSWER BOOKLET.]

National
Qualifications
2018

Mark

X713/76/01

Chemistry
Section 1 — Answer Grid
and Section 2

MONDAY, 21 MAY

9:00 AM – 11:30 AM

Fill in these boxes and read what is printed below.

Full name of centre

Town

Forename(s)

Surname

Number of seat

Date of birth

Day	Month	Year	Scottish candidate number

Total marks — 100

SECTION 1 — 20 marks

Attempt ALL questions.

Instructions for the completion of Section 1 are given on *Page two*.

SECTION 2 — 80 marks

Attempt ALL questions.

You may refer to the Chemistry Data Booklet for Higher and Advanced Higher.

Write your answers clearly in the spaces provided in this booklet. Additional space for answers and rough work is provided at the end of this booklet. If you use this space you must clearly identify the question number you are attempting. Any rough work must be written in this booklet. You should score through your rough work when you have written your final copy.

Use **blue** or **black** ink.

Before leaving the examination room you must give this booklet to the Invigilator; if you do not, you may lose all the marks for this paper.

The questions for Section 1 are contained in the question paper X713/76/02.

Read these and record your answers on the answer grid on *Page three* opposite.

Use **blue** or **black** ink. Do NOT use gel pens or pencil.

1. The answer to each question is **either** A, B, C or D. Decide what your answer is, then fill in the appropriate bubble (see sample question below).

2. There is **only one correct** answer to each question.

3. Any rough working should be done on the additional space for answers and rough work at the end of this booklet.

Sample question

To show that the ink in a ball-pen consists of a mixture of dyes, the method of separation would be:

    A   fractional distillation

    B   chromatography

    C   fractional crystallisation

    D   filtration.

The correct answer is **B** — chromatography. The answer **B** bubble has been clearly filled in (see below).

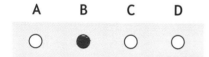

Changing an answer

If you decide to change your answer, cancel your first answer by putting a cross through it (see below) and fill in the answer you want. The answer below has been changed to **D**.

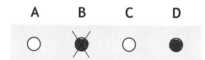

If you then decide to change back to an answer you have already scored out, put a tick (✓) to the **right** of the answer you want, as shown below:

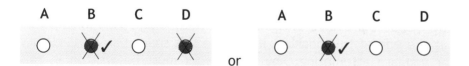

SECTION 1 — Answer Grid

	A	B	C	D
1	○	○	○	○
2	○	○	○	○
3	○	○	○	○
4	○	○	○	○
5	○	○	○	○
6	○	○	○	○
7	○	○	○	○
8	○	○	○	○
9	○	○	○	○
10	○	○	○	○
11	○	○	○	○
12	○	○	○	○
13	○	○	○	○
14	○	○	○	○
15	○	○	○	○
16	○	○	○	○
17	○	○	○	○
18	○	○	○	○
19	○	○	○	○
20	○	○	○	○

[BLANK PAGE]

DO NOT WRITE ON THIS PAGE

Page five

[Turn over for next question

DO NOT WRITE ON THIS PAGE

MARKS | DO NOT WRITE IN THIS MARGIN

SECTION 2 — 80 marks
Attempt ALL questions

1. The elements of group 7 in the periodic table are known as the halogens.

    (a) Going down group 7 the electronegativity of the halogens decreases.

        (i) State what is meant by the term *electronegativity*.   **1**

        (ii) Explain why electronegativity values decrease going down group 7.   **1**

    (b) Explain **fully** why the boiling points of the halogens increase going down group 7.

        In your answer you should name the intermolecular forces involved.   **3**

MARKS | DO NOT WRITE IN THIS MARGIN

2. The elements sodium to argon form the third period of the periodic table.

   (a) Explain the decrease in atom size going across the third period from sodium to argon.   **1**

   (b) Elements in the third period of the periodic table form chlorides.

   The structures of three of these chlorides are shown.

   (i) Circle the structure of the molecule above that contains **bonds** with the lowest polarity.   **1**

   (An additional diagram, if required, can be found on *Page thirty-seven.*)

   (ii) Explain **fully** why, of these three chlorides, silicon tetrachloride is the most soluble in hexane.   **2**

[Turn over

MARKS | DO NOT WRITE IN THIS MARGIN

2. **(continued)**

   (c) Silicon tetrachloride can be used to make silicon nitride (Si_3N_4), a compound found in many cutting tools.

     (i) Silicon nitride has a melting point of 1900 °C and does not conduct electricity when molten.

        Explain **fully**, in terms of structure and bonding, why silicon nitride has a high melting point.   2

    (ii) An equation for the formation of silicon nitride is shown.

$$3SiCl_4 \quad + \quad 16NH_3 \quad \longrightarrow \quad Si_3N_4 \quad + \quad 12NH_4Cl$$

| mass of one mole = 170·1 g | mass of one mole = 17·0 g | mass of one mole = 140·3 g | mass of one mole = 53·5 g |

        Calculate the atom economy for the formation of silicon nitride.   2

MARKS | DO NOT WRITE IN THIS MARGIN

2.   (continued)

(d) Aluminium, another element in the third period, also forms a chloride. Aluminium chloride is prepared by reacting aluminium metal and chlorine gas.

Chlorine gas is produced by the reaction between hydrochloric acid and sodium hypochlorite. The chlorine is then passed over heated aluminium foil, forming aluminium chloride as a hot gas. The hot aluminium chloride gas and unreacted chlorine gas are passed into a flask where the aluminium chloride cools to a fine white powder.

For safety it is important that any unreacted chlorine gas can escape from the flask.

(i) Complete a labelled diagram to show an apparatus suitable for carrying out this preparation.   **2**

(An additional diagram, if required, can be found on *Page thirty-seven*).

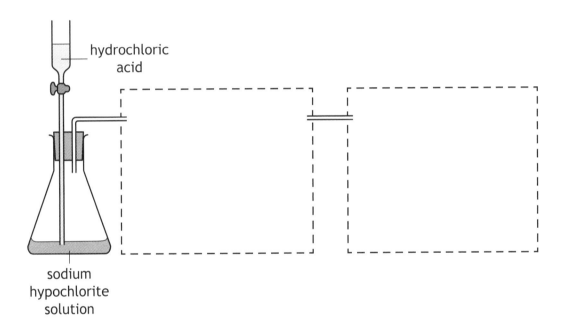

(ii) Explain why the aluminium foil needs to be heated at the start of the preparation, despite the reaction being highly exothermic.   **1**

[Turn over

MARKS | DO NOT WRITE IN THIS MARGIN

3. Methyl benzoate is commonly added to perfumes as it has a pleasant smell.

A student carries out a reaction to produce methyl benzoate using the following apparatus.

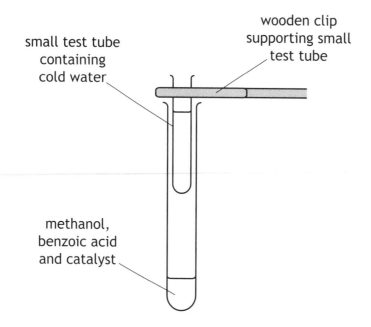

(a) The reaction mixture needs to be heated.

Describe a safe method of heating a flammable mixture.   1

(b) Suggest a reason why there is a small test tube filled with cold water in the neck of the tube containing the reaction mixture.   1

MARKS | DO NOT WRITE IN THIS MARGIN

3.   (continued)

(c)   The chemical reaction involved in the experiment is shown.

$C_6H_5COOH(s)$ + $CH_3OH(\ell)$ $\rightarrow$ $C_6H_5COOCH_3(\ell)$ +   X
benzoic acid   methyl benzoate

mass of one   mass of one   mass of one
mole = 122 g   mole = 32 g   mole = 136 g

(i)   Name product X.   1

(ii)   In a laboratory experiment, a student used 5·0 g of benzoic acid and 2·5 g of methanol to produce methyl benzoate.

Explain why benzoic acid is the limiting reactant.

You must include calculations in your answer.   2

(iii)   The student produced 3·1 g of methyl benzoate from 5·0 g of benzoic acid. Benzoic acid costs £39·80 for 500 g.

Calculate the cost, in £, of the benzoic acid needed to make 100 g of methyl benzoate using the student's method.   2

MARKS | DO NOT WRITE IN THIS MARGIN

4. 3-Methylbutanal is a compound that is found in low concentrations in many types of food. The structure of 3-methylbutanal is shown.

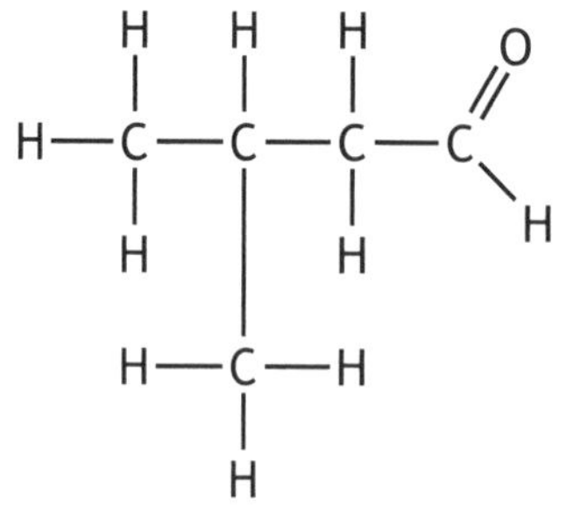

(a) Draw a structural formula for a ketone that is an isomer of 3-methylbutanal.

1

(b) Name a reagent which could be used to distinguish between 3-methylbutanal and a ketone.

1

(c) Name the strongest intermolecular force that occurs between 3-methylbutanal molecules.

1

MARKS | DO NOT WRITE IN THIS MARGIN

4. (continued)

(d) 3-Methylbutanal is found in olive oil.   2

Explain **fully** what can happen to 3-methylbutanal that will cause the olive oil to develop an unpleasant taste.

(e) 3-Methylbutanal can be used as a reactant in the production of other compounds. One reaction scheme involving 3-methylbutanal is shown.

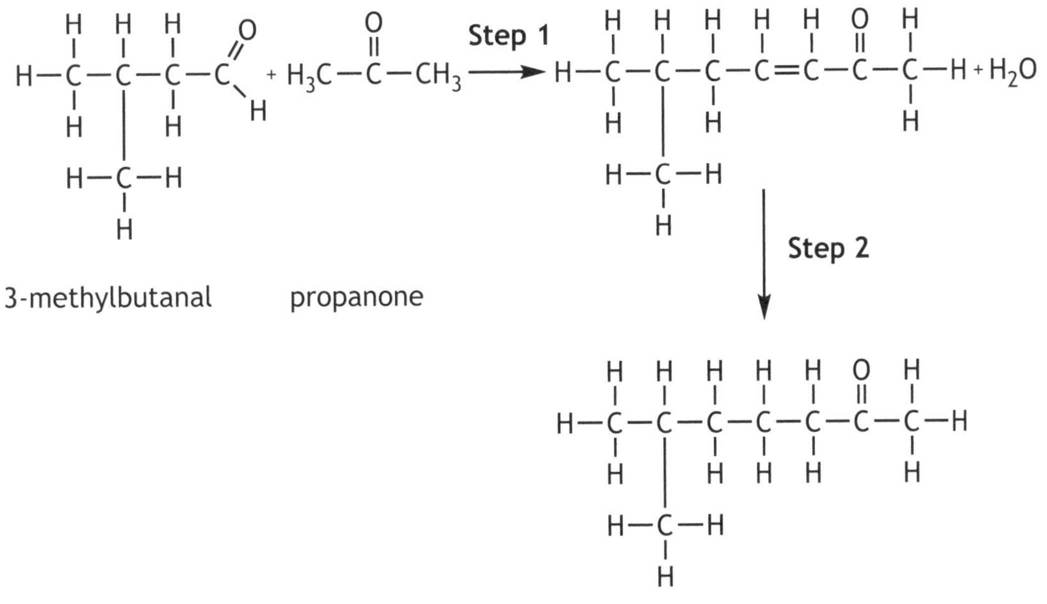

3-methylbutanal   propanone

product A

(i) Explain why **step 1** is described as a condensation reaction.   1

(ii) Give the systematic name for **product A**.   1

MARKS | DO NOT WRITE IN THIS MARGIN

5. Many chemical compounds are related to each other by their structural features, the way they are made and how they are used.

Using your knowledge of chemistry, describe the relationships between fats, oils, detergents, soaps and emulsifiers.

3

[Turn over for next question

DO NOT WRITE ON THIS PAGE

MARKS | DO NOT WRITE IN THIS MARGIN

6. Skin creams contain many different chemicals.

   (a) Retinol (vitamin A) promotes cell regeneration.

   One method of supplying retinol to the skin is by using a skin cream containing the compound retinyl palmitate.

$$C_{15}H_{31}-\overset{\overset{\displaystyle O}{\|}}{C}-O-C_{20}H_{29}$$

   retinyl palmitate

   Retinyl palmitate is absorbed into the skin and then broken down to form retinol.

   (i) Name the type of reaction that occurs when retinyl palmitate is broken down to form retinol.

   1

   (ii) Write a molecular formula for retinol.

   1

   (b) Skin creams often contain vitamin E to prevent damage to the skin caused by free radicals.

   (i) Describe how free radicals are formed.

   1

6. (b) (continued)

(ii) Hydroxyl free radicals (•OH) can attack fatty acids present in cell membranes. One step in the chain reaction is shown below.

$$C_{18}H_{31}O_2 \quad + \quad •OH \quad \rightarrow \quad C_{18}H_{30}O_2• \quad + \quad H_2O$$

State the name given to this step in the chain reaction.   1

(iii) The antioxidant vitamin E is a free radical scavenger.

State how free radical scavengers prevent further chain reactions.   1

[Turn over

MARKS | DO NOT WRITE IN THIS MARGIN

6. (continued)

(c) Palmitoyl pentapeptide-4 is also used in skin creams.

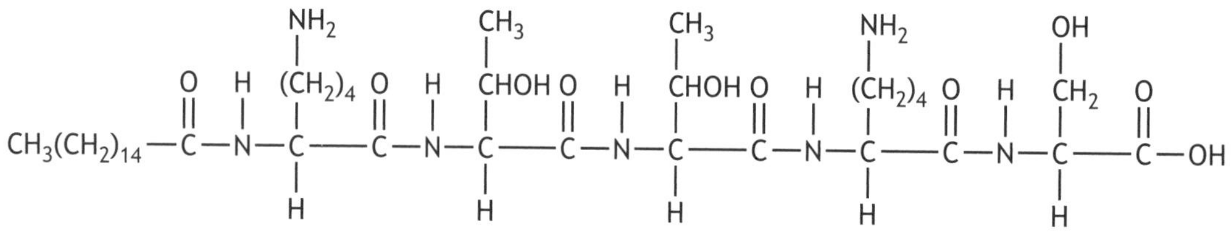

(i) Circle a peptide link in the above structure. **1**

(An additional diagram, if required, can be found on *Page thirty-seven.*)

(ii) Palmitoyl pentapeptide-4 is formed from palmitic acid and three different amino acids.

Molecule	*Number of molecules used to form one molecule of palmitoyl pentapeptide-4*
palmitic acid	1
threonine	2
serine	1
lysine	2

Draw a structural formula for the amino acid serine. **1**

MARKS | DO NOT WRITE IN THIS MARGIN

7. Terpenes consist of joined isoprene units (2-methylbuta-1,3-diene). They are classified by the number of isoprene units in the molecule.

Class of terpene	Number of isoprene units
hemiterpene	1
monoterpene	2
sesquiterpene	3
diterpene	4
triterpene	6

(a) Myrcene and humulene are terpenes present in hops which give beer its characteristic flavour and aroma.

(i) Circle an isoprene unit on the myrcene structure below.   1

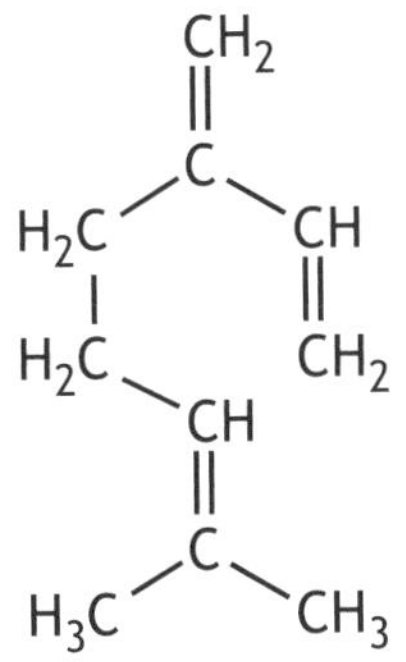

$$CH_2$$
$$\|$$
$$C$$
$$H_2C \quad\quad CH$$
$$| \quad\quad\quad \|$$
$$H_2C \quad\quad CH_2$$
$$CH$$
$$\|$$
$$C$$
$$H_3C \quad\quad CH_3$$

(An additional diagram, if required, can be found on *Page thirty-eight*.)

(ii) Humulene has the molecular formula $C_{15}H_{24}$.

Name the class of terpene to which humulene belongs.   1

[Turn over

MARKS | DO NOT WRITE IN THIS MARGIN

7. **(continued)**

(b) (i) Squalene, a triterpene, is included in some flu vaccines to enhance the body's immune response. A single dose of flu vaccine contains 10·69 mg of squalene.

Calculate the mass of squalene required to produce a batch of 500 000 doses of flu vaccine.

Your answer must be given in kg.

2

(ii) Squalane is a fully saturated hydrocarbon used in skin moisturising cream.

Squalane can be made by the reaction of squalene with hydrogen.

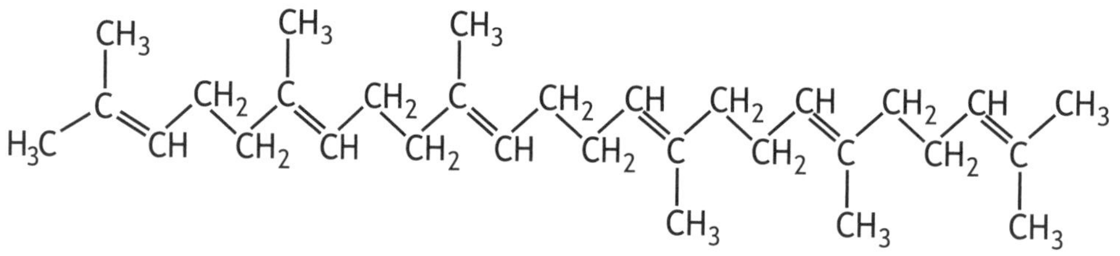

squalene

State the number of moles of hydrogen needed to fully saturate one mole of squalene to produce one mole of squalane.

1

MARKS | DO NOT WRITE IN THIS MARGIN

7. (continued)

(c) The monoterpene limonene, found in lemon oil, can be converted into the alcohol, terpineol.

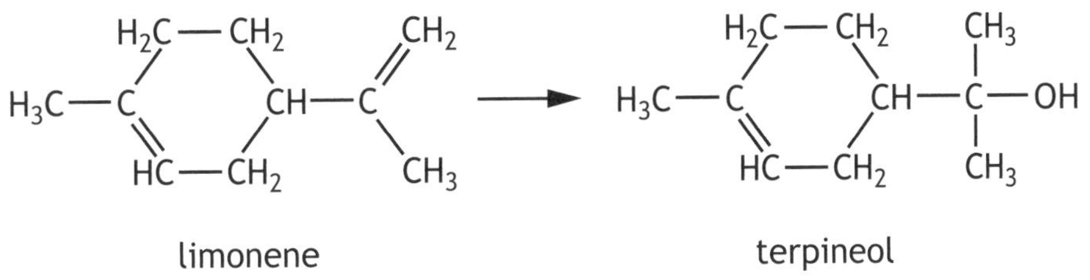

limonene   terpineol

(i) Name the type of reaction taking place.   1

(ii) When terpineol is heated with copper(II) oxide, no reaction takes place.

Explain why no reaction takes place.   1

[Turn over

MARKS | DO NOT WRITE IN THIS MARGIN

8. The alkynes are a homologous family of hydrocarbons.

(a) The simplest member of the family is ethyne, C_2H_2, used in welding torches.

$$H—C\equiv C—H$$

Ethyne can be produced from ethane.

Using bond enthalpies and mean bond enthalpies from the data book, calculate the enthalpy change, in $kJ\,mol^{-1}$, for this reaction.　　2

(b) Hess's Law can be used to calculate the enthalpy change for reactions that do not normally take place, such as the formation of propyne from its elements.

$$3C(s) \quad + \quad 2H_2(g) \quad \rightarrow \quad C_3H_4(g)$$

Calculate the enthalpy change, in $kJ\,mol^{-1}$, for this reaction using the following information.　　2

$C(s) + O_2(g) \rightarrow CO_2(g)$		$\Delta H = -394\,kJ\,mol^{-1}$
$H_2(g) + \frac{1}{2}O_2(g) \rightarrow H_2O(\ell)$		$\Delta H = -286\,kJ\,mol^{-1}$
$C_3H_4(g) + 4O_2(g) \rightarrow 3CO_2(g) + 2H_2O(\ell)$		$\Delta H = -1939\,kJ\,mol^{-1}$

MARKS | DO NOT WRITE IN THIS MARGIN

8.   (continued)

(c)   Propyne, C_3H_4 (1 mole = 40 g), has been suggested as a possible rocket fuel.

(i)   The enthalpy of combustion of propyne is $-1939\,kJ\,mol^{-1}$.

Calculate the energy released, in kJ, when 1 kg of propyne is burned completely.   **1**

(ii)   The mass of air required to burn 1 g of fuel can be calculated using the relationship shown.

Mass of air, in g $= 4\cdot3 \times$ mass of oxygen, in g, for complete combustion of 1 g of fuel

Calculate the mass of air, in g, required to burn 1 g of propyne.   **2**

$$C_3H_4(g) \quad + \quad 4O_2(g) \quad \rightarrow \quad 3CO_2(g) \quad + \quad 2H_2O(\ell)$$

MARKS | DO NOT WRITE IN THIS MARGIN

8. (c) (continued)

(iii) The table shows the mass of air required to burn 1 g of different fuels.

Fuel	Mass of 1 mole (g)	Mass of air required to burn 1 g
ethane	30	16·1
propane	44	15·6
methanol	32	6·5
ethanol	46	9·0

Suggest why methanol and ethanol, compared to the other fuels, require less air to burn 1 g.

1

[Turn over for next question

DO NOT WRITE ON THIS PAGE

MARKS | DO NOT WRITE IN THIS MARGIN

9. Ethane-1,2-diol can be made from ethene.

(a) The flow chart of an industrial process to produce ethane-1,2-diol is shown.

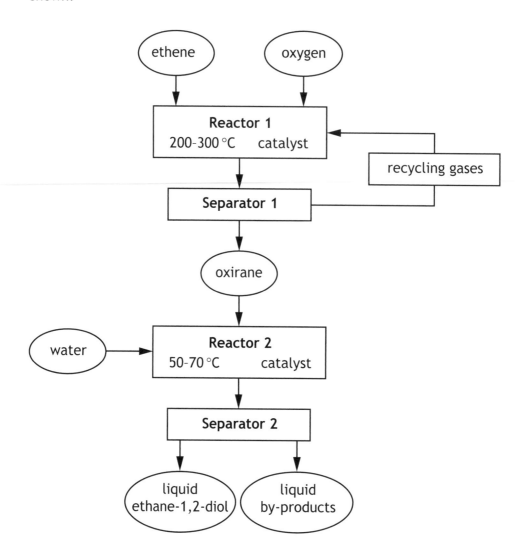

(i) Industrial processes are designed to maximise profit.

Using the flowchart, suggest two ways to maximise profit in this industrial process.

2

MARKS | DO NOT WRITE IN THIS MARGIN

9. (a) (continued)

   (ii) Name the process used in **Separator 2** to separate ethane-1,2-diol from the larger liquid by-products.

1

(b) Explain fully why ethane-1,2-diol is more viscous than propan-1-ol.

2

(c) Draw a structural formula for a diol that contains three carbon atoms.

1

[Turn over

MARKS | DO NOT WRITE IN THIS MARGIN

9. (continued)

(d) Ethane-1,2-diol has been found to be harmful to animals. Treatment for affected animals involves using a 20% ethanol solution.

(i) The 20% ethanol solution is prepared by accurately measuring 20 cm^3 of ethanol and then making up to exactly 100 cm^3 with water.

Describe the procedure which should be used to prepare 100 cm^3 of the 20% ethanol solution.

2

(ii) An affected animal must be treated with 9 doses of 20% ethanol solution. Each dose contains 5 cm^3 of the ethanol solution for every kilogram body mass of the animal.

Calculate the total volume, in cm^3, of the 20% ethanol solution needed to treat a 3·5 kg animal.

1

MARKS | DO NOT WRITE IN THIS MARGIN

9. **(d)** **(continued)**

(iii) Ethane-1,2-diol is harmful because it is oxidised in the body to form glycolic acid.

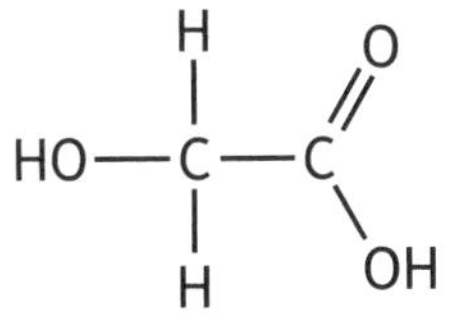

glycolic acid

(A) Draw a structural formula for another possible product of oxidation of ethane-1,2-diol.   **1**

(B) Glycolic acid can be neutralised by sodium hydroxide to form sodium glycolate.

Give a formula for sodium glycolate.   **1**

[Turn over

MARKS DO NOT WRITE IN THIS MARGIN

10. The molar volume (in units of litres per mole) is the same for all gases at the same temperature and pressure.

Using your knowledge of chemistry, suggest how the molar volume of gases could be measured and compared. Any suitable chemicals and apparatus can be used. Some suggested chemicals and apparatus are given below.

3

Chemicals	Apparatus
hydrochloric acid	gas syringe
zinc	measuring cylinder
magnesium	delivery tube
calcium	stoppers
water	500 cm^3 flask
sodium carbonate	vacuum pump
calcium carbonate	balance
cylinder of nitrogen	cork ring
cylinder of hydrogen	burette
cylinder of carbon dioxide	filter funnel

10. (continued)

[Turn over

MARKS | DO NOT WRITE IN THIS MARGIN

11. Iodine is required for a healthy diet. Food grown in certain parts of the world is low in iodine. To prevent iodine deficiency in people's diets, table salt can be 'iodised' by the addition of very small quantities of potassium iodide, KI.

The number of moles of iodide in a sample of salt can be determined by the following procedure.

Step 1

Prepare a standard salt solution by dissolving an accurately weighed sample of iodised salt (50.0 g) in water to give a final volume of 250 cm^3.

Step 2

Transfer 50 cm^3 of salt solution to a conical flask and add excess bromine solution to convert the iodide ions to iodine.

Step 3

Titrate the iodine (I_2) released with sodium thiosulfate solution ($Na_2S_2O_3$).

(a) Describe a procedure to accurately weigh out a 50.0 g sample of iodised table salt.

1

(b) The overall equation for the reaction of bromine solution with iodide ions is shown.

$$2I^-(aq) + Br_2(aq) \longrightarrow I_2(aq) + 2Br^-(aq)$$

Write the ion-electron equation for the oxidation reaction.

1

MARKS | DO NOT WRITE IN THIS MARGIN

11. (continued)

(c) Three samples were prepared as described in **step 2**. Each sample was titrated with $0.0010 \, mol \, l^{-1}$ sodium thiosulfate solution.

The results are shown below.

Sample	Volume of sodium thiosulfate (cm³)
1	10·0
2	9·4
3	9·6

(i) Calculate the average volume, in cm^3, of sodium thiosulfate solution that should be used to determine the number of moles of iodine released.   **1**

(ii) Calculate the number of moles of iodine released from $50 \, cm^3$ of the standard salt solution.   **2**

$$I_2(aq) \ + \ 2Na_2S_2O_3(aq) \ \longrightarrow \ 2NaI(aq) \ + \ Na_2S_4O_6(aq)$$

[Turn over

12. Many modern antiseptics are based on phenol. The table shows the germ-killing power of some phenol compounds.

(a)

Compound	Structure	Germ-killing power (relative to phenol)
phenol		1·0
4-methylphenol		2·5
2-chlorophenol		3·6
4-ethylphenol		7·5
2,4-dichlorophenol		13·0
4-propylphenol		20·0
2,4,6-trichlorophenol		23·0

MARKS | DO NOT WRITE IN THIS MARGIN

12. (a) (continued)

(i) Suggest two ways in which structural features increase germ-killing power of phenol compounds.

2

(ii) The names of the phenol compounds in the table are derived from their structures using the following rules.

Phenol is used as the parent name for the compound.

1. The –OH functional group is assigned as being on carbon 1 of the ring.

2. The ring can be numbered clockwise or anticlockwise to assign numbers to the other atoms or groups. The numbers should be assigned so that the lowest possible numbers are used.

3. If two or more identical atoms or groups are present, use one of the prefixes di, tri or tetra.

4. The names of the atoms or groups attached to the ring are listed alphabetically (ignoring the prefixes for alphabetical purposes).

Using these rules, name this molecule.

1

[Turn over

MARKS | DO NOT WRITE IN THIS MARGIN

12. **(continued)**

(b) There are different methods of producing phenol.

(i) In the early 1900s, phenol was produced by the following reaction.

$$C_6H_6 + H_2SO_4 + 2NaOH \rightarrow C_6H_5OH + Na_2SO_3 + 2H_2O$$

benzene   phenol

mass of one mole = 78·0 g   mass of one mole = 94·0 g

Calculate the mass of phenol, in kg, produced from 117 kg of benzene if the percentage yield is 90%.

2

(ii) Phenol is now usually produced by the Cumene Process.

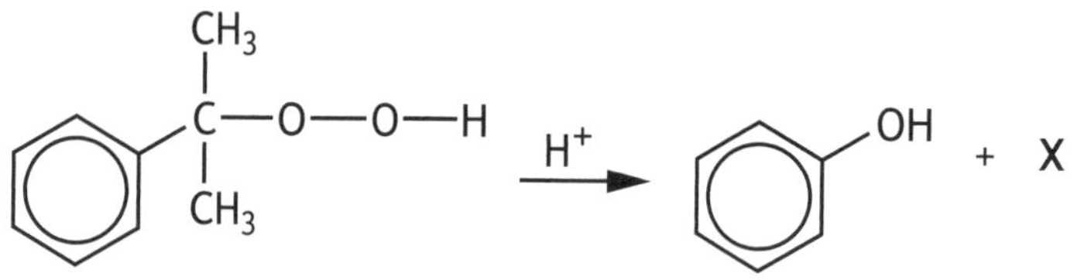

cumene hydroperoxide   phenol

Name the other product, **X**, formed in the Cumene Process.

1

[END OF QUESTION PAPER]

ADDITIONAL SPACE FOR ANSWERS AND ROUGH WORK

ADDITIONAL DIAGRAM FOR USE IN QUESTION 2 (b)

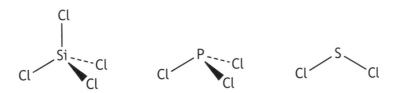

ADDITIONAL DIAGRAM FOR USE IN QUESTION 2 (d) (i)

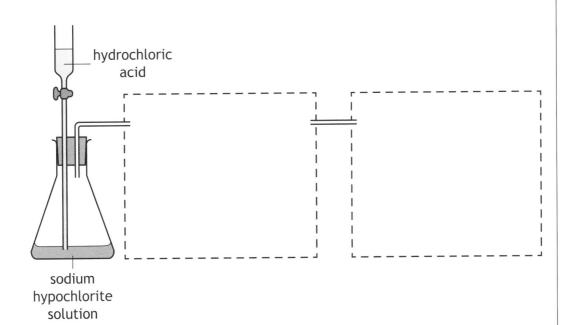

ADDITIONAL DIAGRAM FOR USE IN QUESTION 6 (c) (i)

$CH_3(CH_2)_{14}$—C—N—C—C—N—C—C—N—C—C—N—C—C—N—C—C—OH

MARKS | DO NOT WRITE IN THIS MARGIN

ADDITIONAL SPACE FOR ANSWERS AND ROUGH WORK

ADDITIONAL DIAGRAM FOR USE IN QUESTION 7 (a) (i)

ADDITIONAL SPACE FOR ANSWERS AND ROUGH WORK

MARKS | DO NOT WRITE IN THIS MARGIN

ADDITIONAL SPACE FOR ANSWERS AND ROUGH WORK

2018 Specimen Question Paper

National
Qualifications
SPECIMEN ONLY

S813/76/12

Chemistry
Paper 1 — Multiple choice

Date — Not applicable

Duration — 40 minutes

Total marks — 25

Attempt ALL questions.

You may use a calculator.

Instructions for the completion of Paper 1 are given on *Page two* of your answer booklet S813/76/02.

Record your answers on the answer grid on *Page three* of your answer booklet.

You may refer to the Chemistry Data Booklet for Higher and Advanced Higher.

Space for rough work is provided at the end of this booklet.

Before leaving the examination room you must give your answer booklet to the Invigilator; if you do not, you may lose all the marks for this paper.

Total marks — 25

Attempt ALL questions

1. Which of the following elements, at room temperature, could be described as monatomic?

    A   Argon

    B   Boron

    C   Iodine

    D   Sulfur

2. The table shows the first three ionisation energies of aluminium.

Ionisation energy (kJ mol^{-1})		
1st	2nd	3rd
578	1817	2745

    Using this information, what is the enthalpy change, in kJ mol^{-1}, for the following reaction?

    $$Al^{3+}(g) \ + \ 2e^- \ \rightarrow \ Al^+(g)$$

    A   +2167

    B   −2167

    C   +4562

    D   −4562

3. Which element has the greatest attraction for bonding electrons?

    A   Bromine

    B   Chlorine

    C   Lithium

    D   Sodium

4. Which of the following chlorides is likely to have the most ionic character?

    A $BeCl_2$

    B $CaCl_2$

    C $CsCl$

    D $LiCl$

5. Which of the following elements would have the strongest London dispersion forces?

   A   Argon

   B   Chlorine

   C   Nitrogen

   D   Oxygen

6. The shapes of some common molecules are shown below and each contains at least one polar bond.

   Which molecule is non-polar?

   A   H—Cl

   B

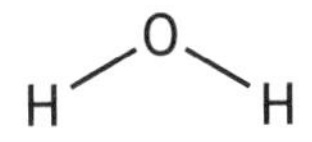

   C   O=C=O

   D

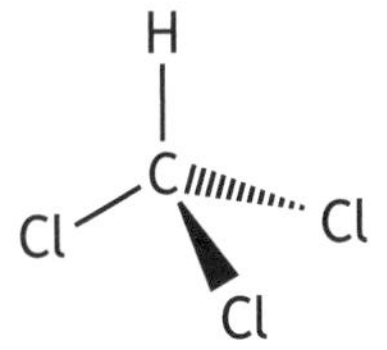

7. Which of the following is an isomer of hexan-2-ol?

   A CH_3—CH_2—CH_2—CH_2—CH—OH
                                    |
                                    CH_3

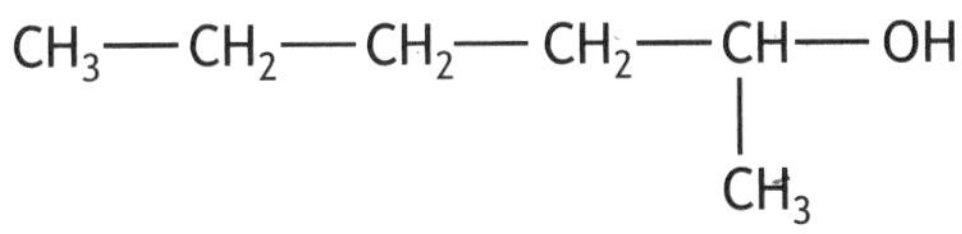

   B

   C CH_3—CH —CH_2—CH_2—CH_2—CH_3
               |
               OH

   D CH_3—CH_2—CH—CH—CH_3
                      | |
                      CH_3 OH

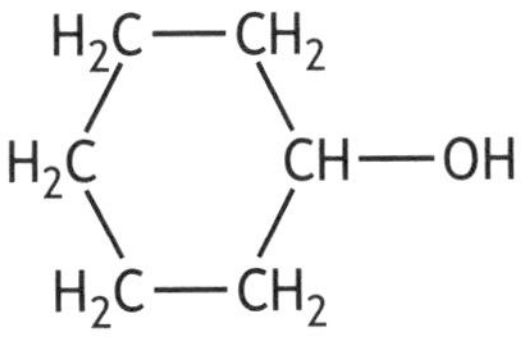

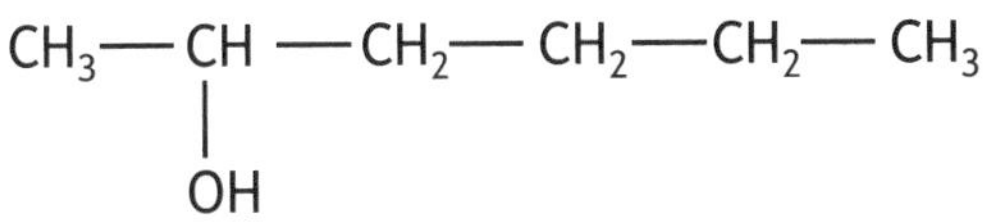

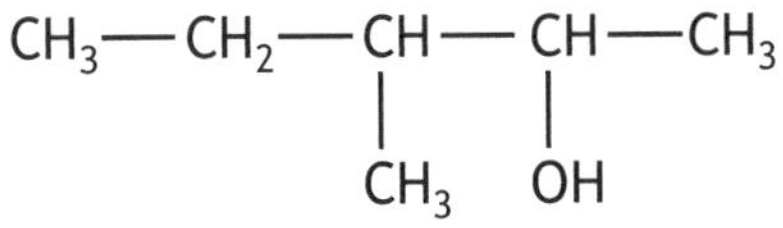

[Turn over

8. Aspirin and oil of wintergreen are used in medicine. Their structures are shown below.

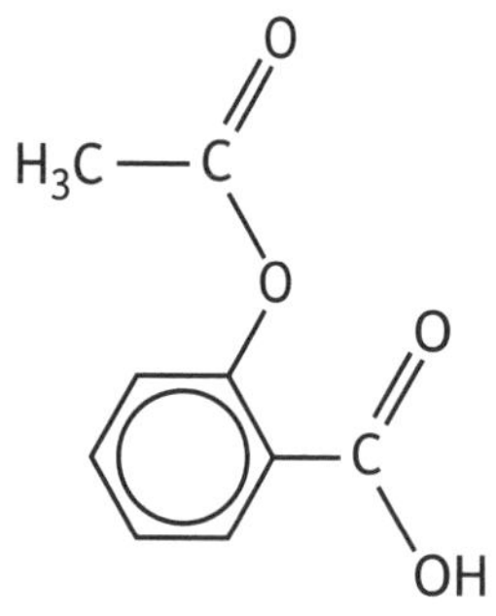

aspirin 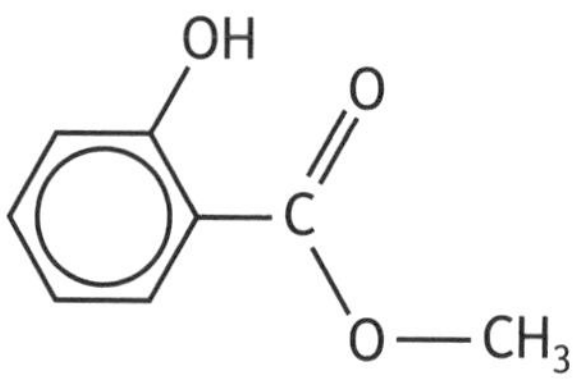   oil of wintergreen

Identify the term which can be applied to aspirin but **not** to oil of wintergreen.

A   Aldehyde

B   Ketone

C   Ester

D   Carboxylic acid

9. The structure of caryophyllene, which can be extracted from clove oil, is

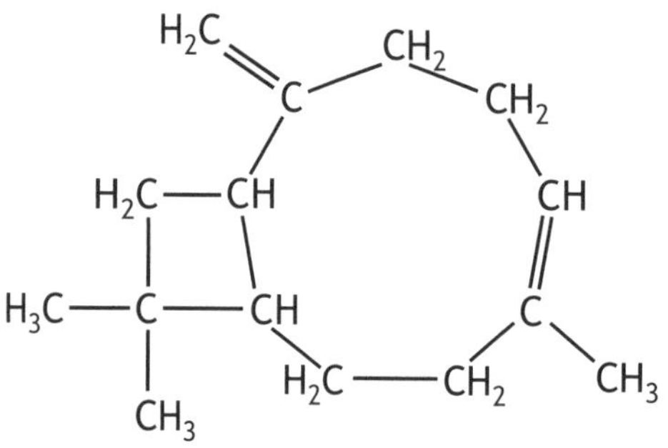

Which of the following would be the best solvent for extracting caryophyllene?

A CH_3—CH_2—CH_2—CH_2—CH_2—CH_3

B CH_3—CH_2—CH_2—CH_2—CH_2—CHO

C CH_3—CH_2—CH_2—CO—CH_2—CH_3

D HO—CH_2—CH_2—CH_2—CH_2—CH_2—CH_3

10. In α-amino acids the amino group is on the carbon atom next to the carboxyl group.

Which of the following is an α-amino acid?

A H_3C—CH—COOH
                   |
              H_2C—NH_2

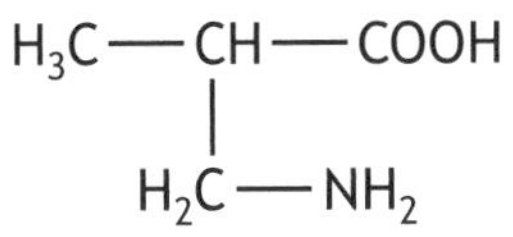

B H_2C—CH—COOH
         | |
        SH NH_2

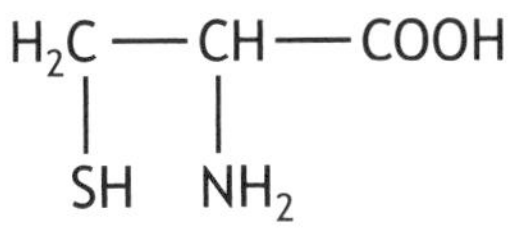

C

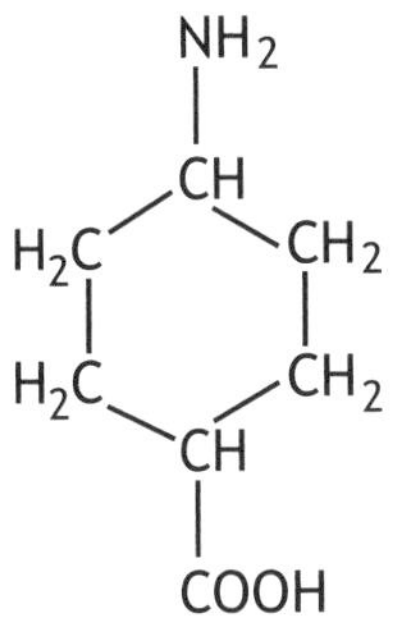

D

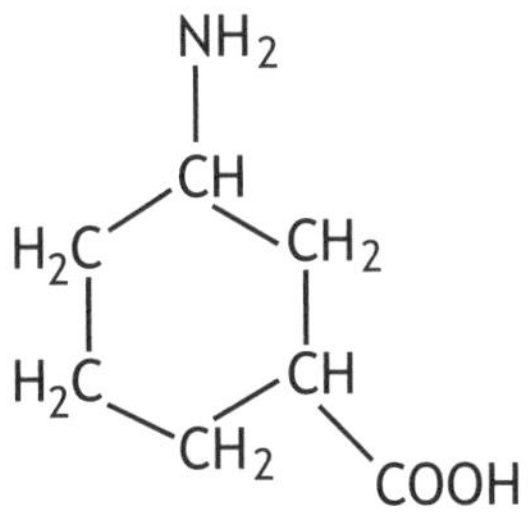

[Turn over

11. The 2-pyrones are esters used as flavourings and in perfumes. The name '2-pyrone' comes from the carbonyl group being in position **2** in the structure shown.

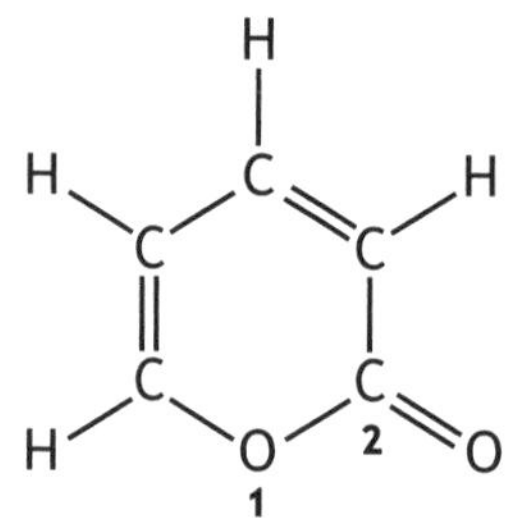

Which of the following structures is the pyrone responsible for the smell of chocolate, 4-hydroxy-6-methyl-2-pyrone?

A

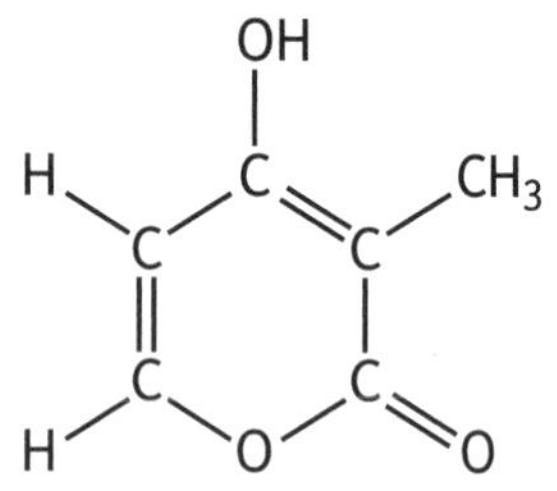

B

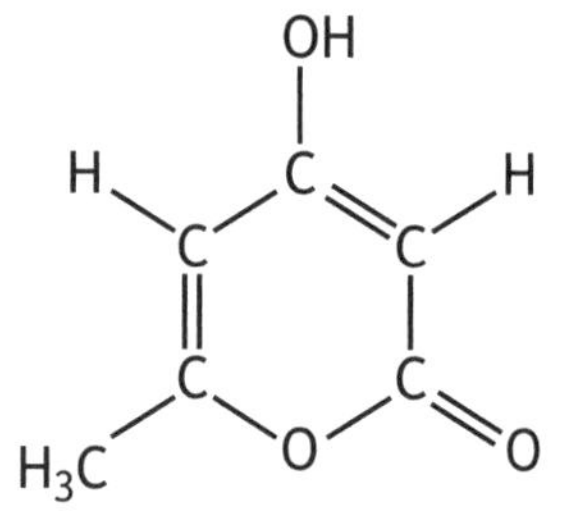

C

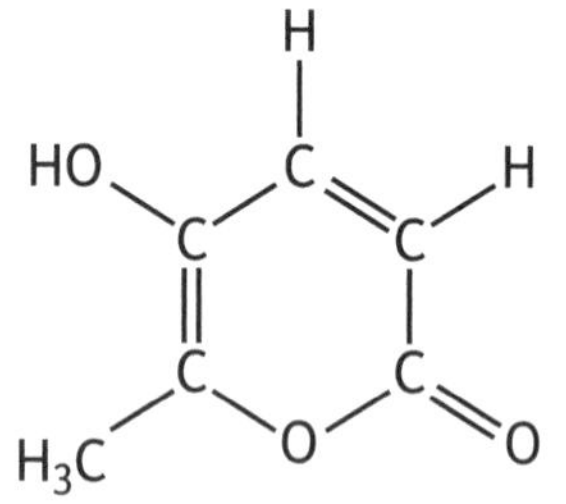

D

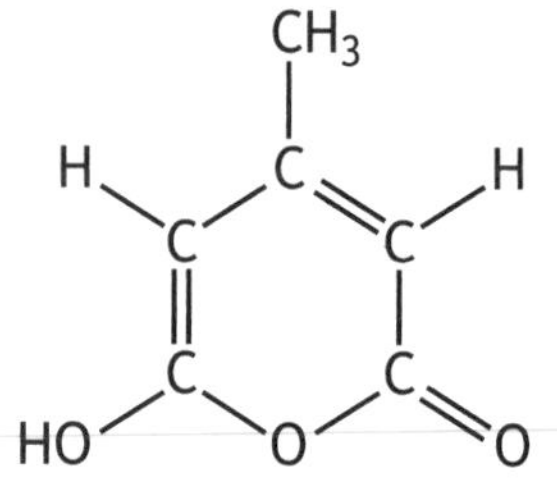

12. Which of the following reactions can be classified as reduction?

A CH_3CH_2OH $\rightarrow$ CH_3COOH

B $CH_3CH(OH)CH_3$ $\rightarrow$ CH_3COCH_3

C $CH_3CH_2COCH_3$ $\rightarrow$ $CH_3CH_2CH(OH)CH_3$

D CH_3CH_2CHO $\rightarrow$ CH_3CH_2COOH

13. Which of the following structural formulae represents a tertiary alcohol?

A

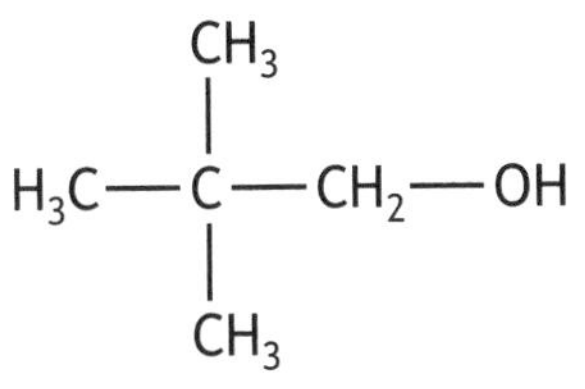

$$H_3C-\underset{\underset{CH_3}{|}}{\overset{\overset{CH_3}{|}}{C}}-CH_2-OH$$

B

$$H_3C-\underset{\underset{OH}{|}}{\overset{\overset{CH_3}{|}}{C}}-CH_2-CH_3$$

C

$$H_3C-CH_2-CH_2-\underset{\underset{OH}{|}}{\overset{\overset{OH}{|}}{C}}-CH_3$$

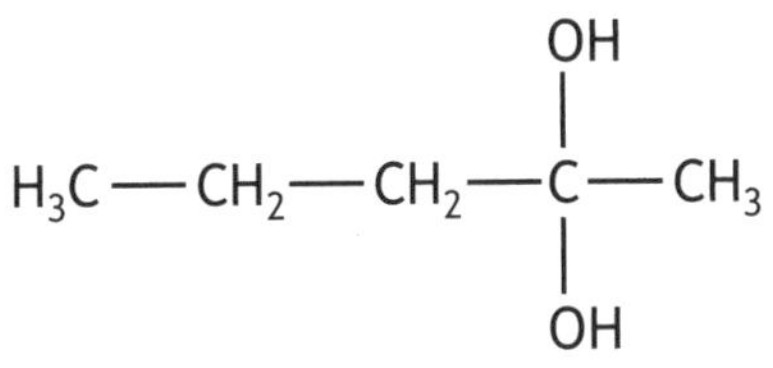

D

$$H_3C-CH_2-\underset{\underset{OH}{|}}{\overset{\overset{H}{|}}{C}}-CH_2-CH_3$$

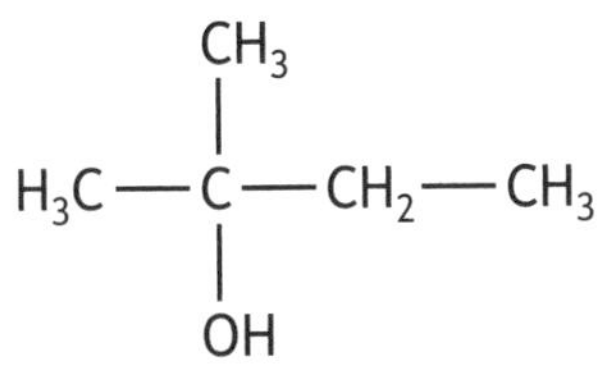

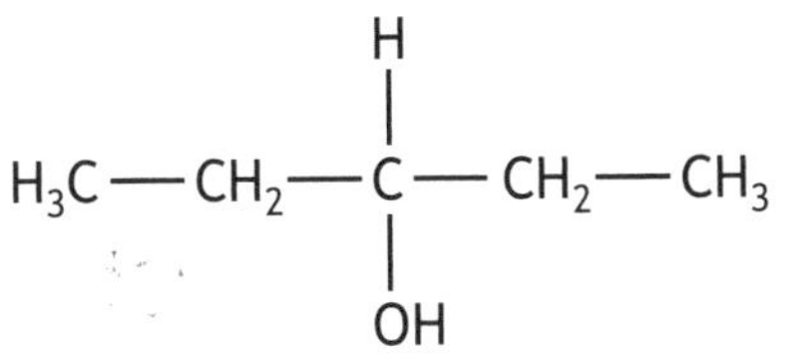

[Turn over

14. A mixture of sodium bromide and sodium sulfate is known to contain 10 moles of sodium and 4 moles of bromide ions.

How many moles of sulfate ions are present?

A 3
B 4
C 5
D 6

15. 4·6 g of sodium is added to 4·8 litres of oxygen to form sodium oxide.

When the reaction is complete, which of the following statements will be true?

(Take the volume of 1 mole of oxygen to be 24 litres.)

A 0·10 mol of oxygen will be left unreacted.
B 0·10 mol of sodium will be left unreacted.
C 0·15 mol of oxygen will be left unreacted.
D 0·20 mol of sodium oxide will be formed.

16. A student obtained a certain volume of carbon dioxide by the reaction of 20 cm³ of 2 mol l⁻¹ hydrochloric acid, HCl, with excess sodium carbonate.

$$2HCl(aq) + Na_2CO_3(aq) \rightarrow 2NaCl(aq) + CO_2(g) + H_2O(\ell)$$

The student carried out a similar experiment using sulfuric acid, H_2SO_4.

$$H_2SO_4(aq) + Na_2CO_3(aq) \rightarrow Na_2SO_4(aq) + CO_2(g) + H_2O(\ell)$$

Which solution of sulfuric acid would give the same final volume of carbon dioxide when added to excess sodium carbonate?

A 10 cm³ of 2 mol l⁻¹
B 20 cm³ of 2 mol l⁻¹
C 10 cm³ of 4 mol l⁻¹
D 20 cm³ of 4 mol l⁻¹

17. In a reversible reaction, equilibrium is reached when

    A   molecules of reactants stop changing into molecules of products

    B   the concentrations of reactants and products are equal

    C   the concentrations of reactants and products are constant

    D   the activation energy of the forward reaction is equal to that of the reverse reaction.

18. Ethanol is manufactured by reacting ethene with steam.

    $$C_2H_4(g) \ + \ H_2O(g) \ \rightleftharpoons \ C_2H_5OH(g) \qquad \Delta H = -46\,kJ\,mol^{-1}$$

    Which set of conditions would give the best yield of ethanol at equilibrium?

    A   High temperature, low pressure

    B   High temperature, high pressure

    C   Low temperature, high pressure

    D   Low temperature, low pressure

19. When copper carbonate is reacted with excess acid, carbon dioxide is produced.
    The curves shown were obtained under different conditions.

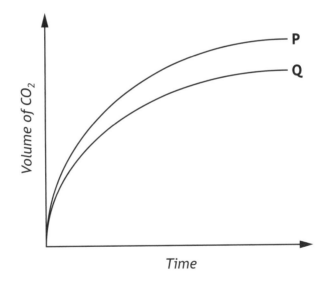

    The change from **P** to **Q** could be brought about by

    A   increasing the concentration of the acid

    B   decreasing the mass of copper carbonate

    C   decreasing the particle size of the copper carbonate

    D   adding a catalyst.

[Turn over

20. The potential energy diagram for a reaction is shown.

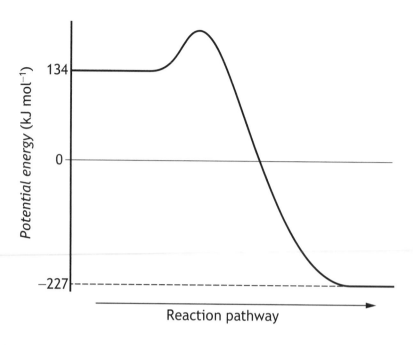

ΔH, in kJ mol^{-1}, for the forward reaction is

A   +361

B   -93

C   -227

D   -361

21. Which of the following is **not** a correct statement about the effect of a catalyst?
The catalyst

A   provides energy so that more molecules have successful collisions

B   lowers the energy that molecules need for successful collisions

C   provides an alternative route to the products

D   allows more molecules to have energies greater than the activation energy.

22. Which of the following equations represents an enthalpy of combustion?

A $C_2H_6(g)$ + $3\frac{1}{2}O_2(g)$ → $2CO_2(g)$ + $3H_2O(\ell)$

B $C_2H_5OH(\ell)$ + $O_2(g)$ → $CH_3COOH(\ell)$ + $H_2O(\ell)$

C $CH_3CHO(\ell)$ + $\frac{1}{2}O_2(g)$ → $CH_3COOH(\ell)$

D $CH_4(g)$ + $1\frac{1}{2}O_2(g)$ → $CO(g)$ + $2H_2O(\ell)$

23. $5N_2O_4(\ell) + 4CH_3NHNH_2(\ell) \longrightarrow 4CO_2(g) + 12H_2O(\ell) + 9N_2(g)$ $\Delta H = -5116\,kJ$

The energy released when 2 moles of each reactant are mixed and ignited is

A   2046 kJ

B   2558 kJ

C   4093 kJ

D   5116 kJ.

[Turn over

24. A chemist analysed a mixture of four dyes **A**, **B**, **C** and **D** using gas-liquid chromatography.

In this technique, compounds are separated depending on their polarity, with the most polar having the longest retention times. The chromatogram obtained is shown below.

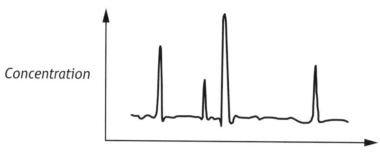

Concentration

Increasing retention time

Which of the following compounds was present in greatest concentration?

Dye	Structure
A	![structure A]
B	![structure B]
C	![structure C]
D	![structure D]

25. Ethanol and ethanoic acid are flammable liquids.

Which of the following diagrams shows the correct set up for the separation of ethanol from ethanoic acid?

A

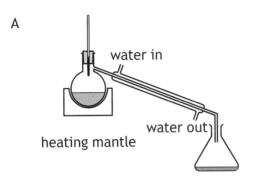

B

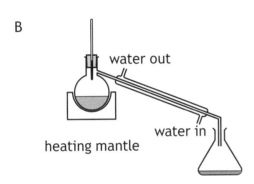

C

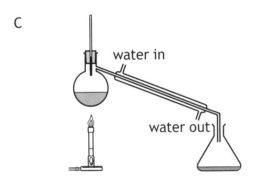

D

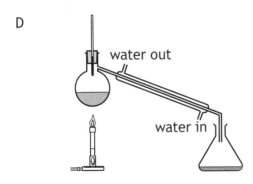

[END OF SPECIMEN QUESTION PAPER]

SPACE FOR ROUGH WORK

Page fourteen

FOR OFFICIAL USE

National
Qualifications
SPECIMEN ONLY

Mark

S813/76/02

Chemistry
Paper 1 — Multiple choice
Answer booklet

Date — Not applicable

Duration — 40 minutes

Fill in these boxes and read what is printed below.

Full name of centre

Town

Forename(s)

Surname

Number of seat

Date of birth
Day   Month   Year

Scottish candidate number

Instructions for the completion of Paper 1 are given on *Page two*.

Record your answers on the answer grid on *Page three*.

Use **blue** or **black** ink.

Before leaving the examination room you must give your answer booklet to the Invigilator; if you do not, you may lose all the marks for this paper.

Paper 1 — 25 marks

The questions for Paper 1 are contained in the question paper S813/76/12.

Read these and record your answers on the answer grid on *Page three*.

Use **blue** or **black** ink. Do NOT use gel pens or pencil.

1. The answer to each question is **either** A, B, C or D. Decide what your answer is, then fill in the appropriate bubble (see sample question below).

2. There is **only one correct** answer to each question.

3. Any rough working should be done on the space for rough work at the end of the question paper S813/76/12.

Sample question

To show that the ink in a ball-pen consists of a mixture of dyes, the method of separation would be:

    A   fractional distillation

    B   chromatography

    C   fractional crystallisation

    D   filtration.

The correct answer is **B** — chromatography. The answer **B** bubble has been clearly filled in (see below).

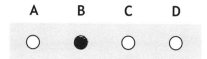

Changing an answer

If you decide to change your answer, cancel your first answer by putting a cross through it (see below) and fill in the answer you want. The answer below has been changed to **D**.

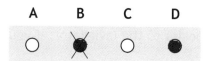

If you then decide to change back to an answer you have already scored out, put a tick (✓) to the **right** of the answer you want, as shown below:

Paper 1 — Answer Grid

	A	B	C	D
1	○	○	○	○
2	○	○	○	○
3	○	○	○	○
4	○	○	○	○
5	○	○	○	○
6	○	○	○	○
7	○	○	○	○
8	○	○	○	○
9	○	○	○	○
10	○	○	○	○
11	○	○	○	○
12	○	○	○	○
13	○	○	○	○
14	○	○	○	○
15	○	○	○	○
16	○	○	○	○
17	○	○	○	○
18	○	○	○	○
19	○	○	○	○
20	○	○	○	○
21	○	○	○	○
22	○	○	○	○
23	○	○	○	○
24	○	○	○	○
25	○	○	○	○

Page four

[BLANK PAGE]

DO NOT WRITE ON THIS PAGE

H

National Qualifications
SPECIMEN ONLY

Mark

S813/76/01

**Chemistry
Paper 2**

Date — Not applicable

Duration — 2 hours 20 minutes

Fill in these boxes and read what is printed below.

Full name of centre

Town

Forename(s)

Surname

Number of seat

Date of birth

Day	Month	Year		Scottish candidate number

Total marks — 95

Attempt ALL questions.

You may use a calculator.

You may refer to the Chemistry Data Booklet for Higher and Advanced Higher.

Write your answers clearly in the spaces provided in this booklet. Additional space for answers and rough work is provided at the end of this booklet. If you use this space you must clearly identify the question number you are attempting. Any rough work must be written in this booklet. Score through your rough work when you have written your final copy.

Use **blue** or **black** ink.

Before leaving the examination room you must give this booklet to the Invigilator; if you do not, you may lose all the marks for this paper.

MARKS | DO NOT WRITE IN THIS MARGIN

Total marks — 95

Attempt ALL questions

1. The periodic table allows chemists to make predictions about the properties of elements.

    (a) The elements lithium to neon make up the second period of the periodic table.

Li	Be	B	C	N	O	F	Ne

    (i) Name an element from the second period that can exist as a covalent network.   **1**

    (ii) Explain why the atoms decrease in size from lithium to neon.   **1**

    (iii) Name the element that is the strongest reducing agent in the second period.   **1**

MARKS | DO NOT WRITE IN THIS MARGIN

1. **(continued)**

(b) On descending group 1 from lithium to caesium, the electronegativity of the elements decreases.

Explain **fully** why the electronegativity of the elements decreases going down group 1.

2

(c) Tin(IV) iodide is a compound formed from a metal element and a non-metal element.

Tin(IV) iodide is a bright orange powder that dissolves easily in non-polar solvents. It has a melting point of 143 °C and a boiling point of 340 °C.

Name the type of bonding **and** structure present in tin(IV) iodide.

1

[Turn over

MARKS | DO NOT WRITE IN THIS MARGIN

2. The table below contains information about some diatomic molecules.

	H—H	H—Cl	Cl—Cl	I—Cl	Br—Br
Boiling point (°C)	−253	−85	−34	97	59
Bond enthalpy (kJ mol^{-1})	436	432	243	211	194

(a) Boiling points can be used to show the effect of intermolecular forces.

Explain **fully** why ICl and Br$_2$ provide good evidence for a fair comparison of the relative strengths of different types of intermolecular force.

3

(b) State which of the diatomic molecules listed in the table above has the strongest covalent bond.

1

MARKS | DO NOT WRITE IN THIS MARGIN

2. (continued)

(c) Hydrogen and chlorine gases were used in an experiment to demonstrate a free radical reaction.

A test-tube was wrapped with black tape leaving a 'window' on one side. The tube was filled with a mixture of hydrogen and chlorine. When a bright light was directed at the tube, the gas mixture exploded and the ball was fired across the room.

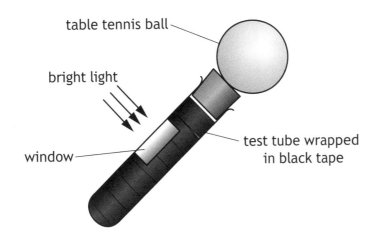

A free radical chain reaction is initiated when light energy causes chlorine radicals to form as shown below.

Initiation   Cl—Cl $\xrightarrow{\text{light}}$ Cl•   +   Cl•

(i) Complete the equations below showing possible propagation and termination steps.   2

Propagation   Cl• + H—H $\longrightarrow$ +

Termination   H• + H• $\longrightarrow$

(ii) Suggest why the test tube was wrapped in black tape.   1

[Turn over

MARKS | DO NOT WRITE IN THIS MARGIN

2. (c) **(continued)**

    (iii) When hydrogen gas and chlorine gas react hydrogen chloride gas is produced.

$$H_2(g) \; + \; Cl_2(g) \; \rightarrow \; 2HCl(g)$$

    Using bond enthalpy values, calculate the enthalpy change, in $kJ\,mol^{-1}$, for the reaction of one mole of hydrogen with one mole of chlorine.

2

(d) Chlorine can be made in a redox reaction between permanganate ions and chloride ions.

The ion-electron equations for the oxidation and reduction reactions are shown below.

$$2Cl^-(aq) \; \rightarrow \; Cl_2(g) \; + \; 2e^-$$

$$MnO_4^-(aq) \; + \; 8H^+(aq) \; + \; 5e^- \; \rightarrow \; Mn^{2+}(aq) \; + \; 4H_2O(\ell)$$

Write a balanced equation for the reaction of permanganate ions with chloride ions to produce chlorine gas.

1

MARKS | DO NOT WRITE IN THIS MARGIN

3. A team of chemists are developing a shower gel.

(a) A suitable fragrance must be created for the shower gel.

(i) To give the gel a fruity smell the chemists are considering adding an ester. They synthesise six isomeric esters. Volunteers smell each ester and give it a rating out of one hundred depending on how fruity the smell is.

Structure	Fruit-smell rating
CH_3-C (=O) $O-CH_2-CH_2-CH_2-CH_2-CH_3$	100
CH_3-C (=O) $O-CH-CH_2-CH_2-CH_3$ with CH_3	34
CH_3-C (=O) $O-C(CH_3)(CH_3)-CH_2-CH_3$	0
CH_3-CH_2-C (=O) $O-CH_2-CH_2-CH_2-CH_3$	92
$CH_3-CH(CH_3)-C$ (=O) $O-CH_2-CH_2-CH_3$	44
$CH_3-C(CH_3)(CH_3)-C$ (=O) $O-CH_2-CH_3$	32

(A) Name the ester with the fruit-smell rating of 92.   1

[Turn over

MARKS | DO NOT WRITE IN THIS MARGIN

3. (a) (i) (continued)

(B)   Shown below are the structures of three more isomers.

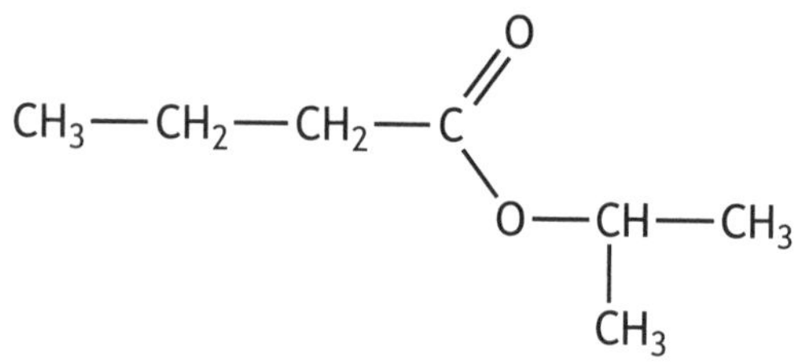

Ester **A**

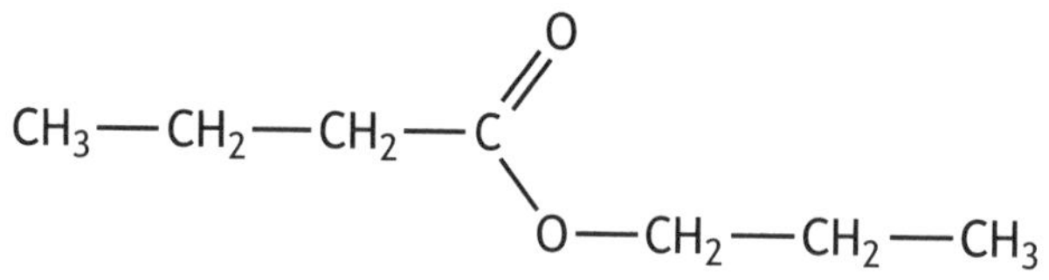

Ester **B**

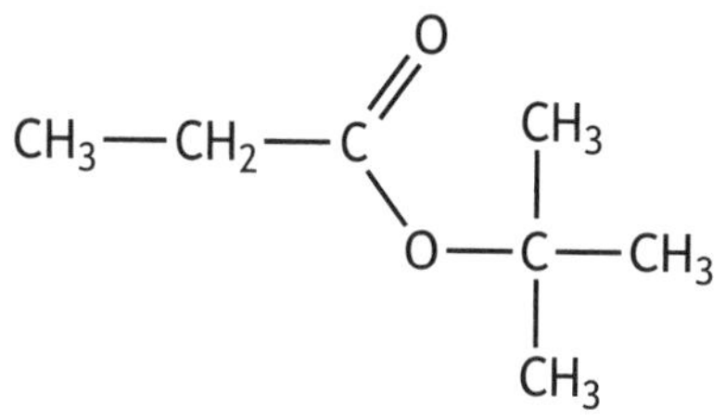

Ester **C**

Arrange these esters in order of **decreasing** fruit-smell rating.   1

Ester ☐   >   Ester ☐   >   Ester ☐

MARKS | DO NOT WRITE IN THIS MARGIN

3. (a) (continued)

(ii) The compound civetone will also be used in the fragrance.

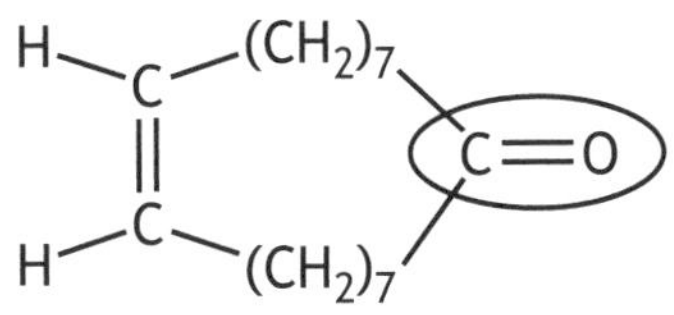

civetone

(A) Name the functional group circled in the structure above.   1

(B) Draw a structural formula for the alcohol that can be oxidised to form civetone.   1

(b) To make the shower gel produce a cold, tingling sensation when applied to the skin, menthol is added.

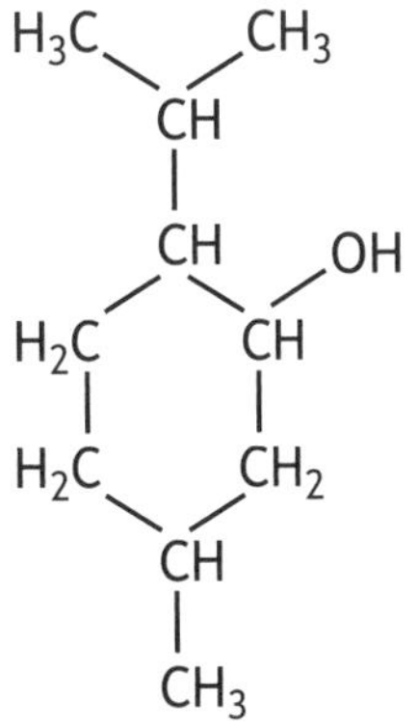

Menthol is based on two isoprene units.

Circle one of the isoprene units on the menthol structure above.   1

(An additional diagram, if required, can be found on *Page thirty-eight*.)

[Turn over

MARKS | DO NOT WRITE IN THIS MARGIN

3. (continued)

(c) Sodium lauryl sulfate, a detergent, is used in the shower gel to give the product cleaning properties.

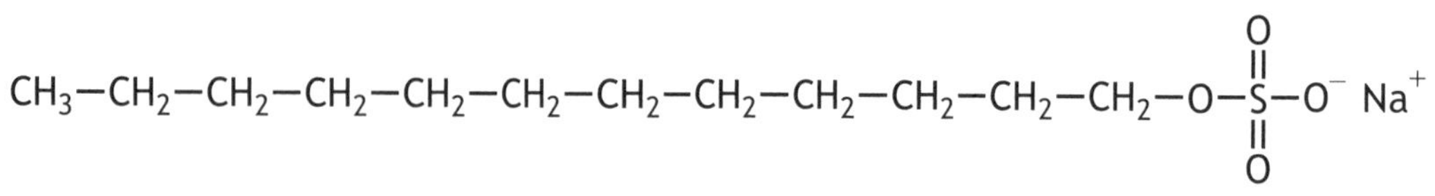

$$CH_3-CH_2-CH_2-CH_2-CH_2-CH_2-CH_2-CH_2-CH_2-CH_2-CH_2-CH_2-O-\overset{O}{\underset{O}{\overset{\|}{\underset{\|}{S}}}}-O^- \; Na^+$$

(i) **Explain fully** the cleaning action of sodium lauryl sulfate.

(You may wish to use diagrams to illustrate your answer.)

3

(ii) Explain why detergents, like sodium lauryl sulfate, are preferable to soap in hard water areas.

1

MARKS | DO NOT WRITE IN THIS MARGIN

3. **(continued)**

(d) Esters and terpenes have been used for thousands of years to create fragrances.

Traces of liquid were discovered in a perfume bottle that belonged to Queen Hatshepsut, ruler of Egypt, over 3500 years ago.

Egyptian perfumes were made by dissolving plant extracts containing pleasant-smelling terpenes and esters in an edible oil. A little ethanol and water may also have been added.

Using your knowledge of chemistry, comment on the possible smell(s) when such a bottle is opened after being stored for thousands of years.   **3**

[Turn over

4. A student carried out some experiments using different edible fats and edible oils.

   (a) The first experiment allowed the iodine number to be determined. The larger the iodine number, the greater the number of carbon-to-carbon double bonds present in the fat or oil.

Fat or oil	Iodine number	Typical molecule found in fat or oil
Olive oil	86	
Shea butter	57	
Linseed oil	173	
Sunflower oil		

MARKS | DO NOT WRITE IN THIS MARGIN

4. (a) (continued)

    (i) Shea butter has the highest melting point of these substances.

       Explain **fully** why the melting point of shea butter is higher than the edible oils.

    3

    (ii) By considering the number of carbon-to-carbon double bonds in each structure, predict the iodine number of sunflower oil.

    1

[Turn over

MARKS | DO NOT WRITE IN THIS MARGIN

4. (continued)

(b) In the second experiment, soap was made by heating triolein obtained from olive oil with sodium hydroxide solution.

$$(C_{17}H_{33}COO)_3C_3H_5 \ + \ 3NaOH \ \rightarrow \ 3C_{17}H_{33}COONa \ + \ X$$

triolein   soap

GFM = 884 g   GFM = 304 g

(i) Name product **X**.   1

(ii) 5·00 g of triolein produced 1·28 g of soap.

Calculate the percentage yield.   3

5. Butan-2-ol is widely used as a solvent.

    (a) In industry butan-2-ol is produced by the hydration of but-2-ene.

$$C_4H_8(g) \;+\; H_2O(g) \;\rightarrow\; C_4H_{10}O(g)$$

    but-2-ene   butan-2-ol

    The enthalpy values for the following reactions are:

$$4C(s) \;+\; 4H_2(g) \qquad\qquad \rightarrow\; C_4H_8(g) \qquad \Delta H = \;\;-7\cdot1\,kJ\,mol^{-1}$$

$$4C(s) \;+\; 5H_2(g) \;+\; \tfrac{1}{2}O_2(g) \;\rightarrow\; C_4H_{10}O(g) \qquad \Delta H = -292\cdot8\,kJ\,mol^{-1}$$

$$H_2(g) \;+\; \tfrac{1}{2}O_2(g) \qquad\qquad \rightarrow\; H_2O(g) \qquad \Delta H = -241\cdot8\,kJ\,mol^{-1}$$

    Using the data above, calculate the enthalpy change, in $kJ\,mol^{-1}$, for the production of butan-2-ol by hydration of but-2-ene.

2

[Turn over

5. (continued)

(b) A chemist investigated the costs invotlved in producing butan-2-ol from propanal using a two-step process.

Step One

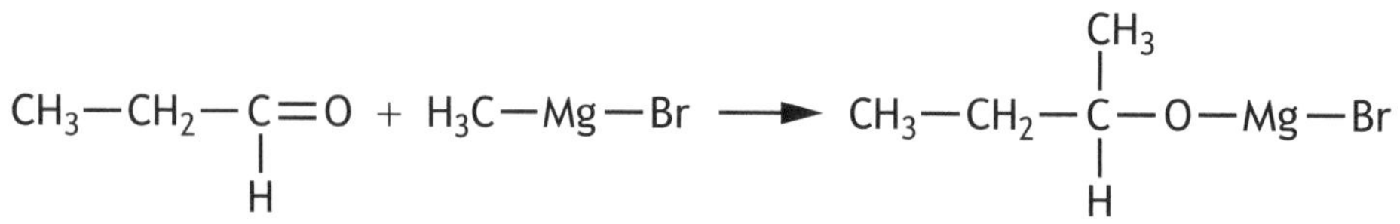

$$CH_3-CH_2-\underset{\underset{H}{|}}{C}{=}O \ + \ H_3C-Mg-Br \ \longrightarrow \ CH_3-CH_2-\underset{\underset{H}{|}}{\overset{\overset{CH_3}{|}}{C}}-O-Mg-Br$$

propanal   methyl magnesium bromide

Step Two

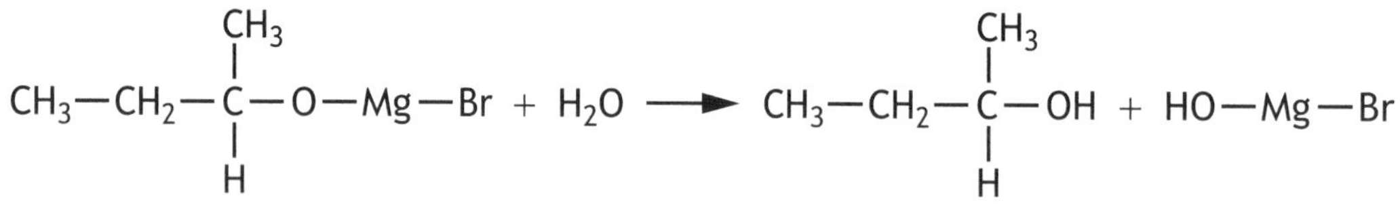

$$CH_3-CH_2-\underset{\underset{H}{|}}{\overset{\overset{CH_3}{|}}{C}}-O-Mg-Br \ + \ H_2O \ \longrightarrow \ CH_3-CH_2-\underset{\underset{H}{|}}{\overset{\overset{CH_3}{|}}{C}}-OH \ + \ HO-Mg-Br$$

butan-2-ol

(i) The chemist made 5·75 g of butan-2-ol using 5·01 g of propanal and 20·0 g of methyl magnesium bromide.

The costs of the chemicals used are shown below.

Propanal	£22·10 for 1 kg
Methyl magnesium bromide	£75·00 for 25 g

Calculate the cost of the chemicals, in £, needed to produce 100 g of butan-2-ol using this method.

2

(ii) This method can be used to produce different alcohols by using other aldehydes in place of propanal.

Name the alcohol produced if this method is repeated using pentanal.

1

MARKS | DO NOT WRITE IN THIS MARGIN

5. **(continued)**

(c) Butan-2-ol can be converted into butanone, another useful solvent.

(i) Name the type of reaction that takes place when butan-2-ol is converted into butanone.

1

(ii) Care must be taken when using butanone as a solvent because it is highly flammable.

The lowest temperature at which butanone will ignite is called its flash point.

For the family of compounds containing butanone, the flash point can be predicted from the number of carbon atoms it contains using the formula:

flash point in °C = (14 × number of carbon atoms) − 59

Calculate the flash point, in °C, for butanone.

1

[Turn over

MARKS | DO NOT WRITE IN THIS MARGIN

6. Chemists have developed cheeses specifically for use in cheeseburgers.

(a) When ordinary cheese is heated, the texture changes as the protein molecules change shape.

Explain fully why protein molecules change shape when they are heated.   2

(b) To make cheese for burgers, ordinary cheese, soluble milk proteins and water are mixed and heated to no more than 82 °C. As the cheese begins to melt, trisodium citrate is added.

(i) Suggest why a water bath was used to heat the mixture.   1

(ii) Trisodium citrate is the salt formed when citric acid is neutralised using a base.

$$H_2C-COOH$$
$$HO-C-COOH$$
$$H_2C-COOH$$

citric acid

Suggest the name of a base that could be used to neutralise citric acid forming trisodium citrate.   1

MARKS | DO NOT WRITE IN THIS MARGIN

6. (b) (continued)

(iii) A section of the structure of a soluble milk protein is shown below.

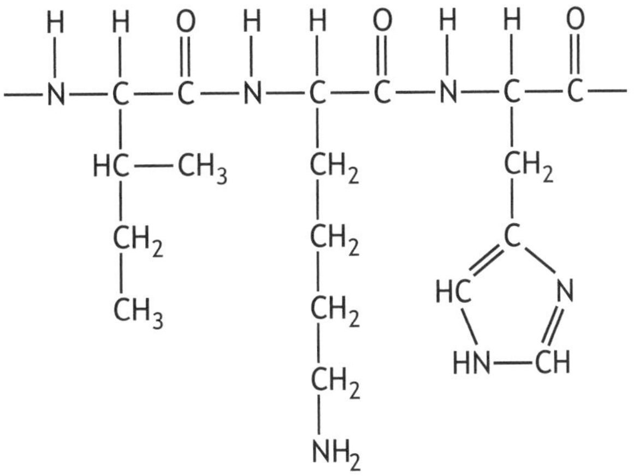

Draw a structural formula for any **one** of the amino acids formed when this section of protein is hydrolysed. 1

(c) Cheese is a source of zinc, an essential element for the body.

The mass of zinc in four 100 g samples taken from a burger cheese was measured.

Sample	*Mass of zinc* (mg)
1	4·0
2	21·7
3	3·9
4	4·1

Calculate the average mass of zinc, in mg, in 100 g of this burger cheese. 1

[Turn over

MARKS | DO NOT WRITE IN THIS MARGIN

6. (continued)

(d) A calorie-free replacement for the fat in cheese can be made by reacting fatty acids with the hydroxyl groups on a molecule of sucrose.

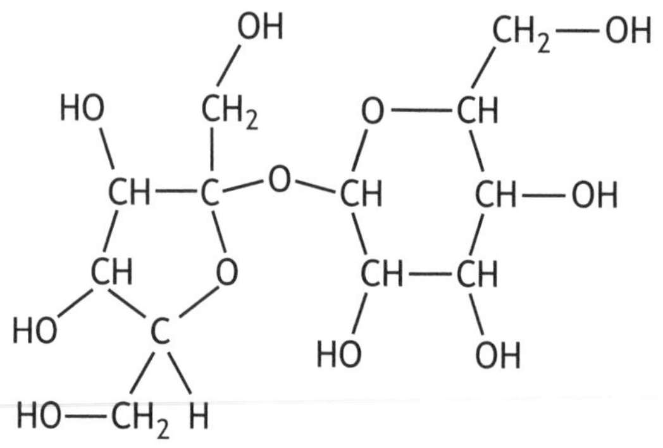

sucrose

State how many fatty acid molecules can react with one molecule of sucrose.

1

MARKS | DO NOT WRITE IN THIS MARGIN

7. Ibuprofen is one of the best-selling painkillers in the UK.

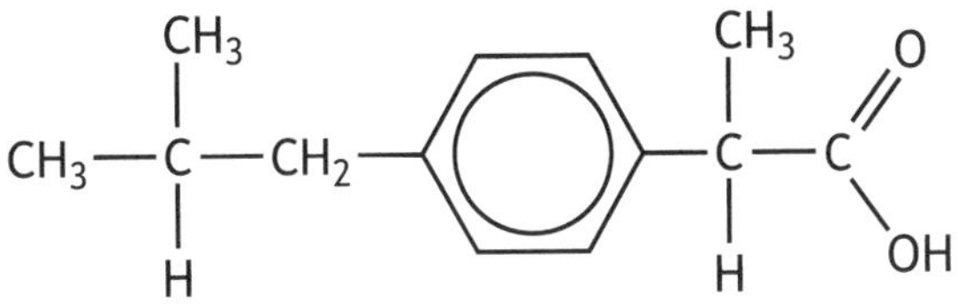

ibuprofen

(a) Ibuprofen tablets should not be taken by people who suffer from acid indigestion.

Name the functional group present in ibuprofen that makes this drug unsuitable for these people.

1

(b) From the 1990s, ibuprofen has been synthesised by a three step process.

The equation below shows the final step of the synthesis.

$$C_{12}H_{17}OH \quad + \quad CO \quad \xrightarrow{\text{Pd catalyst}} \quad C_{12}H_{17}COOH$$

ibuprofen

(i) State the percentage atom economy of this step.

1

[Turn over

MARKS | DO NOT WRITE IN THIS MARGIN

7. (b) (continued)

(ii) The diagram below represents the changing potential energy during this reaction when it is carried out without the palladium catalyst.

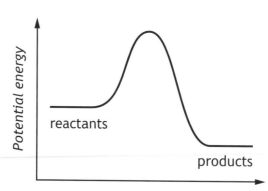

Reaction progress

Add a line to the diagram showing the changing potential energy when the catalyst is used.

1

(An additional diagram, if required, can be found on *Page thirty-eight.*)

(c) Ibuprofen, $C_{12}H_{17}COOH$, is taken for the relief of pain in the form of pills or tablets because it is only slightly soluble in water.

(i) Suggest why ibuprofen is only slightly soluble in water.

1

MARKS | DO NOT WRITE IN THIS MARGIN

7. **(c)** **(continued)**

(ii) Small children can find it difficult to swallow tablets or pills so ibuprofen is supplied as an 'infant formula' liquid.

(A) The 'infant formula' also contains polysorbate 80. Its structure is shown below.

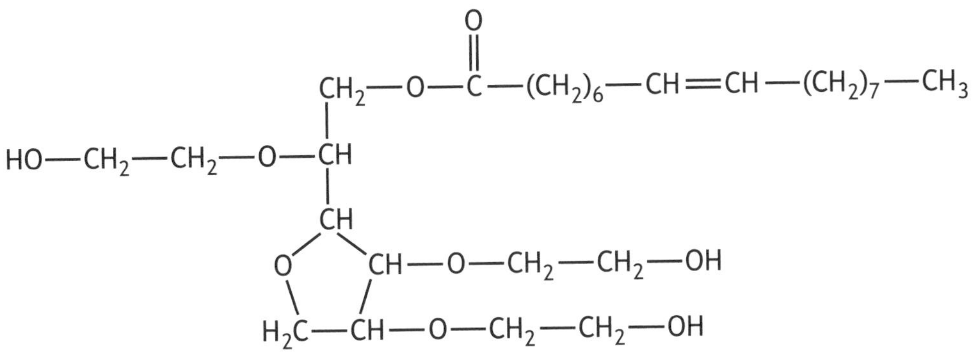

Suggest why polysorbate 80 is included in the 'infant formula'.　1

(B) The 'infant formula' contains $2 \cdot 0$ g of ibuprofen in every $100 \, cm^3$ of liquid.

The recommended dose for treating a 6-month-old baby is $0 \cdot 050$ g.

Calculate the volume, in cm^3, of 'infant formula' needed to treat a 6-month-old baby.　1

[Turn over

MARKS | DO NOT WRITE IN THIS MARGIN

8. Ethanol and 2-methylpropan-1-ol are alcohols that can be used as renewable fuels in car engines.

(a) Alcohols tends to absorb water from the air causing corrosion in fuel tanks and engines. Water is absorbed because alcohols can form hydrogen bonds with water molecules.

In the box below, showing a molecule of ethanol, draw a molecule of water and use a dotted line to show where a hydrogen bond exists between the two molecules.

1

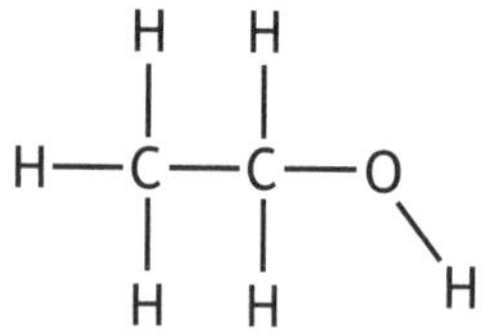

(An additional diagram, if required, can be found on *Page thirty-eight*.)

(b) Draw a structural formula for 2-methylpropan-1-ol.

1

MARKS
DO NOT WRITE IN THIS MARGIN

8. (continued)

(c) A car was fuelled with 15 litres of ethanol. The ethanol burned releasing 351 000 kJ of energy.

Volume of 1 g of 2-methylpropan-1-ol	$1 \cdot 25 \, cm^3$
Energy released when 1 g of 2-methylpropan-1-ol burns	$36 \cdot 1 \, kJ$

Use the data in the table to calculate the volume of 2-methylpropan-1-ol that would burn to release the same quantity of energy.   3

[Turn over

MARKS | DO NOT WRITE IN THIS MARGIN

9. A student carried out an investigation to measure the fluoride and nitrite levels in a water supply.

   (a) The student prepared a set of sodium fluoride solutions of known concentration by diluting a standard solution.

      (i) State what is meant by the term **standard solution**. **1**

      (ii) Calculate the mass, in mg, of sodium fluoride, NaF, needed to make 1 litre of standard solution with a **fluoride ion** concentration of $100\,mg\,l^{-1}$. **2**

      (iii) Describe how the standard solution would be prepared from the weighed sample of sodium fluoride. **3**

      (iv) Suggest why the student should use distilled or deionised water rather than tap water when dissolving the sodium fluoride. **1**

MARKS | DO NOT WRITE IN THIS MARGIN

9. (a) (continued)

(v) The concentration of fluoride ions in a sample of water can be determined by adding the sample to a solution containing a coloured compound. The coloured compound reacts with fluoride ions turning colourless. The higher the concentration of fluoride ions present in a water sample, the paler the colour and the less light is absorbed by the solution.

The graph below shows results for six solutions of known fluoride ion concentration.

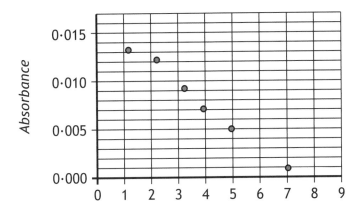

Fluoride ion concentration (mg l^{-1})

Determine the concentration, in mg l^{-1}, of fluoride ions in a water sample that reacted with the coloured compound to form a solution with an absorbance of 0·012.   **1**

[Turn over

MARKS | DO NOT WRITE IN THIS MARGIN

9. **(continued)**

(b) The concentration of nitrite ions, NO_2^-, in the water supply was determined by titrating water samples with acidified permanganate solutions.

The reaction taking place is

$$2MnO_4^-(aq) + 5NO_2^-(aq) + 6H^+(aq) \rightarrow 2Mn^{2+}(aq) + 5NO_3^-(aq) + 3H_2O(\ell)$$

(i) Name the most appropriate piece of laboratory apparatus to measure out $25 \cdot 0 \, cm^3$ samples of water.

1

(ii) $21 \cdot 6 \, cm^3$ of $0 \cdot 015 \, mol \, l^{-1}$ acidified permanganate solution was required to react completely with the nitrite ions in a $25 \cdot 0 \, cm^3$ sample of water.

Calculate the nitrite ion concentration, in $mol \, l^{-1}$, in the water.

Show your working clearly.

3

MARKS | DO NOT WRITE IN THIS MARGIN

10. Soft drinks can contain ingredients such as sweeteners and caffeine.

(a) Aspartame is a sweetener. Its structure is shown below.

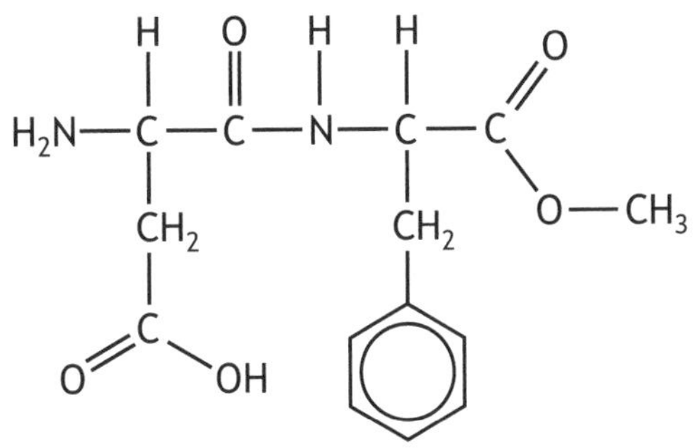

(i) In the stomach, aspartame is hydrolysed by acid to produce two amino acids and an alcohol.

State what is meant by the term 'hydrolysed'.   **1**

(ii) Name the alcohol produced in the hydrolysis reaction.   **1**

(iii) The body cannot make all the amino acids it requires and is dependent on protein in the diet for the supply of certain amino acids.

State the term used to describe the amino acids the body cannot make.   **1**

[Turn over

MARKS | DO NOT WRITE IN THIS MARGIN

10. (continued)

(b) The concentration of caffeine can be found using chromatography.

A chromatogram for a solution containing 50 mg l⁻¹ of caffeine is shown below.

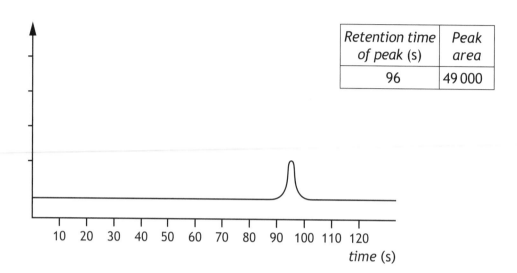

Retention time of peak (s)	Peak area
96	49 000

Results from four caffeine solutions were used to produce the calibration graph below.

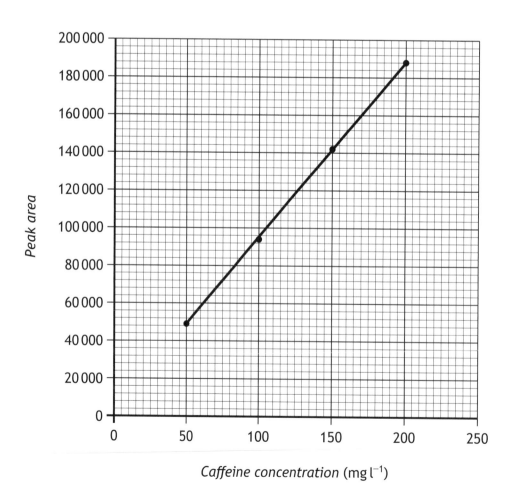

10. (b) (continued)

(i) The chromatogram for soft drink **X** is shown below.

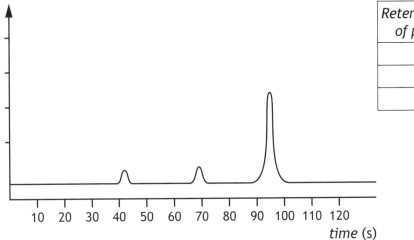

Retention time of peak (s)	Peak area
42	1000
69	1350
96	68 000

Determine the caffeine content, in mg l⁻¹, of soft drink **X**.   1

(ii) The chromatogram for soft drink **Y** is shown below.

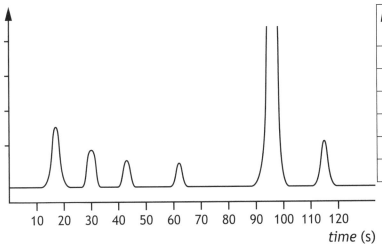

Retention time of peak (s)	Peak area
17	7000
30	4600
43	3000
62	2500
96	- - - -
115	5000

The caffeine content of soft drink **Y** cannot be determined from its chromatogram.

Suggest what could be done to the sample of soft drink **Y** so that the caffeine content could be reliably determined.   1

MARKS | DO NOT WRITE IN THIS MARGIN

11. Hypochlorite bleaches are cleaning products containing the hypochlorite ion, $ClO^-(aq)$, a good oxidising agent.

(a) Hypochlorite bleaches can be made by reacting sodium hydroxide with chlorine. Sodium hypochlorite, NaClO, sodium chloride and water are formed.

Write a balanced equation for the reaction.   **1**

(b) When $ClO^-(aq)$ acts as a bleach, it is reduced to produce the $Cl^-(aq)$ ion.

Complete the ion-electron equation to show the reduction reaction.   **1**

$ClO^-(aq)$ $\rightarrow$ $Cl^-(aq)$

MARKS | DO NOT WRITE IN THIS MARGIN

11. (continued)

(c) In one method that can be used to measure the concentration of hypochlorite ions in a sample of bleach, the bleach sample is reacted with excess hydrogen peroxide.

$$H_2O_2(aq) + ClO^-(aq) \rightarrow H_2O(\ell) + Cl^-(aq) + O_2(g)$$

By measuring the volume of oxygen given off, the concentration of bleach can be calculated.

(i) Draw a diagram showing an assembled apparatus that could be used to react hydrogen peroxide solution with bleach and measure the volume of oxygen gas released.

Your diagram should include labels showing the names and positions of the reacting chemicals and the collected product.   **3**

(ii) 80 cm³ of oxygen gas was produced from 5·0 cm³ of bleach.

Calculate the concentration, in mol l⁻¹, of the hypochlorite ions in the bleach.   **3**

(Take the molar volume of one mole of oxygen to be 24 litres.)

[Turn over

12. Changing the temperature at which a redox reaction is carried out changes the rate of reaction.

    (a) The effect of temperature on reaction rate can be studied using the rate at which acidified potassium permanganate is reduced by oxalic acid.

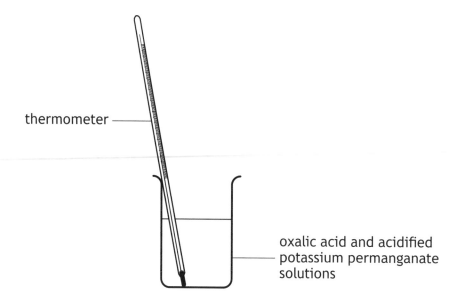

thermometer

oxalic acid and acidified potassium permanganate solutions

   (i) State the colour change that takes place when acidified permanganate ions are reduced.   1

MARKS | DO NOT WRITE IN THIS MARGIN

12. (a) (continued)

    (ii) A student's results are shown on the graph below.

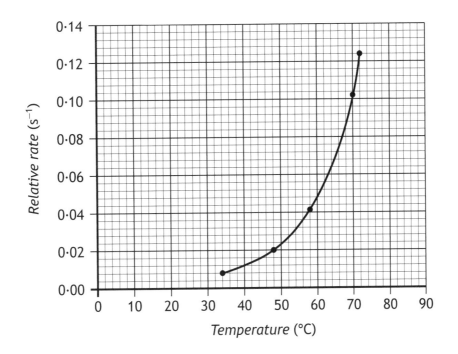

    Calculate the time taken for the reaction, in s, when the reaction is carried out at 40 °C.

2

[Turn over

MARKS | DO NOT WRITE IN THIS MARGIN

12. **(continued)**

(b) (i) Graph 1 shows the distribution of kinetic energy of molecules in a gas at 100 °C.

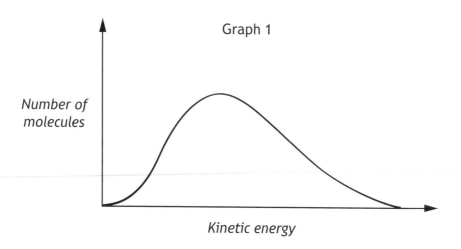

Graph 1

Add a second curve to Graph 1 to show the distribution of kinetic energies at 50 °C.

(An additional graph, if required, can be found on *Page thirty-nine*.)

1

(ii) In Graph 2, the shaded area represents the number of molecules with the required activation energy, E_a.

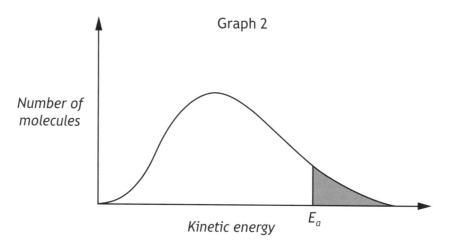

Graph 2

Draw a line to show how a catalyst affects the activation energy.

(An additional graph, if required, can be found on *Page thirty-nine*.)

1

(c) A collision involving molecules with the required energy of activation may **not** result in a reaction.

State a reason for this.

1

13. Cis-platin, $PtN_2H_6Cl_2$, is a widely used anti-cancer drug.

It can be produced in the following **exothermic** reaction.

$$K_2PtCl_4(aq) + 2KI(aq) + 2NH_3(g) + 2AgNO_3(aq) \rightleftharpoons PtN_2H_6Cl_2(aq) + 2AgI(s) + 2KNO_3(aq) + 2KCl(aq)$$

The cost of the chemicals used are shown in the table.

Chemical	Cost per gram (£)
K_2PtCl_4	65·00
KI	0·21
NH_3	0·02
$AgNO_3$	3·90

MARKS | DO NOT WRITE IN THIS MARGIN

Using your knowledge of chemistry, comment on how this process could be carried out to make the production of cis-platin as profitable as possible.   3

[END OF SPECIMEN QUESTION PAPER]

MARKS | DO NOT WRITE IN THIS MARGIN

ADDITIONAL SPACE FOR ANSWERS AND ROUGH WORK

ADDITIONAL DIAGRAM FOR QUESTION 3 (b)

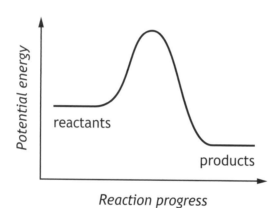

ADDITIONAL DIAGRAM FOR QUESTION 7 (b) (ii)

ADDITIONAL DIAGRAM FOR QUESTION 8 (a)

ADDITIONAL SPACE FOR ANSWERS AND ROUGH WORK

ADDITIONAL GRAPH FOR QUESTION 12 (b) (i)

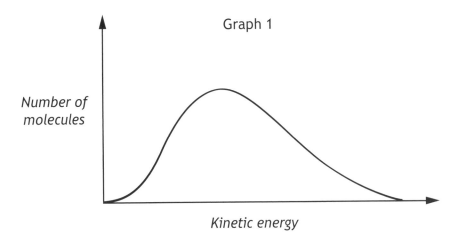

Graph 1

ADDITIONAL GRAPH FOR QUESTION 12 (b) (ii)

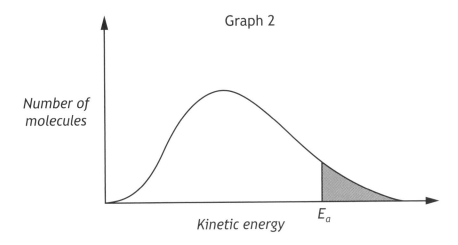

Graph 2

ADDITIONAL SPACE FOR ANSWERS AND ROUGH WORK

MARKS | DO NOT WRITE IN THIS MARGIN

ADDITIONAL SPACE FOR ANSWERS AND ROUGH WORK

[BLANK PAGE]

DO NOT WRITE ON THIS PAGE

HIGHER

Answers

HIGHER CHEMISTRY 2017

Section 1

Question	Answer	Max Mark
1.	A	1
2.	D	1
3.	C	1
4.	B	1
5.	D	1
6.	C	1
7.	B	1
8.	C	1
9.	A	1
10.	C	1
11.	B	1
12.	C	1
13.	B	1
14.	B	1
15.	C	1
16.	A	1
17.	D	1
18.	A	1
19.	D	1
20.	B	1

Section 2

1. (a) Silicon　　　　　　　　　　　　　　　　(1 mark)

   (b) (i) Increasing/greater/stronger/higher nuclear charge (holds electron more tightly)

      OR

      Increasing number of protons　　　　(1 mark)

      (ii) $Mg^+(g) \longrightarrow Mg^{2+}(g) + e^-$　(1 mark)

      (iii) Fourth ionisation energy involves removal of an electron from an electron shell which is inner/full (whole)/(more) stable/closer to the nucleus

      OR

      fourth electron is removed from an electron shell which is inner/full (whole)/(more) stable/closer to the nucleus.

      OR

      removing third electron is taking from an outer/a part full shell

      OR

      taking an electron from a full shell requires more energy (than removing from a part full shell)

      OR

      taking an electron from a part full shell requires less energy (than removing from a full shell)

      OR

fourth electron is less shielded than the third electron

OR

third electron is more shielded than the fourth electron　　　　　　　　　　　(1 mark)

   (c) **1 mark:** Correctly identify that there are stronger/more (Van der Waals) forces between chlorine (molecules) than between the argon (atoms)

   1 mark: Correctly identifying that the van der Waals forces present in both these elements are London dispersion forces

   1 mark: Chlorine molecules (Cl_2) have more electrons than argon atoms (Ar).

   　　　　　　　　　　　　Maximum mark: 3

2. (a) (i) I-I bond is weaker/has a lower bond enthalpy value (so will break more easily)

      OR

      I_2 (151 kJ mol^{-1}) is less than H_2 (436 kJ mol^{-1}), (so will break more easily).　　(1 mark)

      (ii) Peak of curve should be further to the right and no higher than the original line.　(1 mark)

      (iii) (A) Equilibrium will shift to the reactant side/left (hand side).　　　　　　(1 mark)

      (B) There are the same/equal volume/number of moles/molecules (of gases) on each side (of the equation).

      OR

      Pressures of reactants and products are equal.　　　　　　　　　　　　　(1 mark)

      (iv) (A) Activated complex　　　　　(1 mark)

      (B) −9·6 (kJ) If candidate has calculated from graph values

      OR

      −9 (kJ) If candidate has calculated using bond enthalpies

      Answer must include the negative sign　　　　　　　　(1 mark)

      (C) Decrease/lower it　　　　　(1 mark)

   (b) (i) To keep the concentration (of the reactants) constant.

      OR

      Adding water will change/affect/dilute/decrease the concentration (of the reactants)

      OR

      To keep the total volume constant.　(1 mark)

      (ii) 122·1 (accept 122) (s)　　　　(1 mark)

      (iii) The number of (successful) collisions will decrease.

      OR

      Less chance of (successful) collisions

      OR

      The frequency of (successful) collisions will decrease.　　　　　　　　　(1 mark)

3. This is an open ended question

   1 mark: The student has demonstrated, at an appropriate level, a limited understanding of the chemistry involved. The candidate has made some statement(s) at which is/are relevant to the situation, showing that at least a little of the chemistry within the problem is understood.

2 marks: The student has demonstrated, at an appropriate level, a reasonable understanding of the chemistry involved. The student makes some statement(s) which is/are relevant to the situation, showing that the problem is understood.

3 marks: The maximum available mark would be awarded to a student who has demonstrated, at an appropriate level, a good understanding of the chemistry involved. The student shows a good comprehension of the chemistry of the situation and has provided a logically correct answer to the question posed. This type of response might include a statement of the principles involved, a relationship or an equation, and the application of these to respond to the problem. This does not mean the answer has to be what might be termed an 'excellent' answer or a 'complete' one.

Maximum mark: 3

4. (a) (i) Pentan-1-ol (1 mark)

(ii)

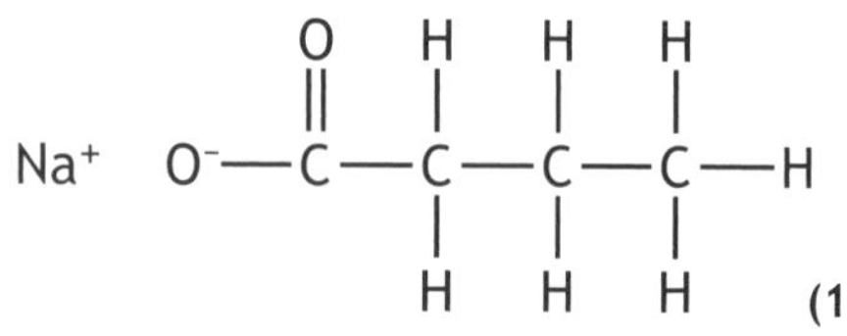

(1 mark)

(b) (i) ester (1 mark)

(ii) soap (1 mark)

(iii) 395 or –395 (kJ) (2 marks)

Partial marking — one mark can be awarded for:

the correct application of number of moles of stearic acid

eg

10/284 × 623 or 0·0352 × 623

(=21·94)   (=21·93)

or

10/284 × 18 or 0·0352 × 18

(=0·634)   (=0·634)

OR

the correct application of the stoichiometry

eg

the energy change for 1 mole of stearic acid as

623 × 18 = 11214 (kJ)

or

284 g ⟷ 623 × 18   Maximum mark: 2

5. (a) (i) Diagram shows a workable method of bubbling through concentrated sulfuric acid. (1 mark)

Diagram for appropriate gas collection method i.e. using a gas syringe or upward displacement of air. (1 mark)

Maximum mark: 2

(ii) Calculating that 0·05 moles HCl would require 0·025 moles sodium sulfite and there are only 0·00317 moles of sodium sulfite

OR

Calculating that 0·00317 moles of sodium sulfite would require 0·00634 moles of HCl and there are 0·05 moles of HCl

Partial marking:

1 mark awarded for correct arithmetical calculation of moles of Na_2SO_3 (= 0·00317 mol) **AND** HCl = 0·05 mol)

OR

Calculating that 3·15 g sodium sulfite would be needed to react with 50 cm³ hydrochloric acid and there are only 0·4 g of sodium sulfite

Partial marking:

1 mark awarded for correct arithmetical calculation of moles of acid (0·05) and correct application of stoichiometry to either reactant.

OR

Calculating that 6·3 cm³ of (1 M) HCl would be needed to react with 0·4 g of sodium sulfite and there are 50 cm³ (1M) HCl

Partial marking:

1 mark awarded for correct arithmetical calculation of moles of sodium sulfite (0·00317) and correct application of stoichiometry to either reactant. (2 marks)

(b) –1075 (kJ mol⁻¹) (2 marks)

Partial marking — treat as two concepts either would be acceptable for 1 mark

Evidence of understanding of reversal for third equation only in order to achieve the target equation.

Reversal of additional equations would be taken as cancelling

OR

evidence of understanding of multiplying for second equation by 2 in order to achieve the target equation. Multiplication of additional equations would be taken as cancelling. (2 marks)

(c) (i) 163 – 167 inclusive (g l⁻¹) (1 mark)

(ii) **1 mark** for carbon dioxide is non-polar due to its shape/dipoles cancelling out **and** sulfur dioxide is polar due to its shape/dipoles not cancelling out

1 mark for an explanation which links polarity of CO_2 and SO_2 molecules to the polarity of water   Maximum marks: 2

6. (a) (i)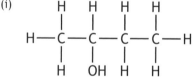

(1 mark)

(ii) (A) Reactants or products are flammable/could catch fire. (1 mark)

(B) orange to green/blue-green/blue (1 mark)

(C) Tertiary (1 mark)

(iii) (A) Butanoic acid

OR

(2-)methylpropanoic acid (1 mark)

(B) $C_4H_9OH + H_2O \longrightarrow C_4H_8O_2 + 4H^+ + 4e^-$ (1 mark)

(b) (i) 2-methylpentanal (1 mark)

(ii) Any temperature between 166 and 181 (°C) (1 mark)

(iii) (More) branching lowers the boiling point (of isomeric aldehydes). (1 mark)

(iv) Silver mirror/silver precipitate (1 mark)

(c) (Permanent) dipole to (permanent) dipole (1 mark)

7. (a) Rinse beaker and transfer the rinsings/washings
to the flask   **(1 mark)**

(b) (i) The reaction is self-indicating.

OR

Potassium permanganate can act as its own
indicator.

OR

Reaction changes colour.   **(1 mark)**

(ii) To provide H^+ ions for the reaction.   **(1 mark)**

(iii) (A) **1 mark** for any of the following

- first titre is a rough (or approximate)
result/practice

- first titre is not accurate/not reliable/
rogue

- first titre is too far away from the others

- you take average of concordant/close
results

(B) 0·0582 (mol l⁻¹)   **(3 marks)**

Partial marks can be awarded using a
scheme of two "concept" marks.

1 mark for knowledge of the relationship
between moles, concentration and volume.
This could be shown by any <u>one</u> of the
following steps:

- Calculation of moles MnO_4^- solution eg
0·02 × 0·01455 = 0·000291

- Calculation of concentration of Fe^{2+}
solution eg 0·001455/0·025

- Insertion of correct pairings of values
for concentration and volume in a valid
titration formula eg

$$\frac{0\cdot02 \times 14\cdot55}{n_1} = \frac{C_{Fe^{2+}} \times 25\cdot0}{n_2}$$

1 mark for knowledge of relationship
between moles of MnO_4^- and Fe^{2+}. This
could be shown by one of the following
steps:

- Calculation of moles Fe^{2+} from moles
MnO_4^- — eg 0·000291 × 5 = 0·001455

- Insertion of correct stoichiometric values
in a valid titration formula eg

$$\frac{0\cdot02 \times 14\cdot55}{1} = \frac{C_{Fe^{2+}} \times 25\cdot0}{5}$$

Maximum marks: 3

(C) A solution of accurately/exactly/precisely
known concentration   **(1 mark)**

(D) Pipette   **(1 mark)**

(c) 14 mg, 14·06 mg, 0·01406 g   **(1 mark)**

(d) 24%, 24·3%   **(2 marks)**

Partial marks

1 mark awarded for

30 g would contain 3·6 mg

1 mark for

$$\frac{\text{any calculated mass}}{14\cdot8} \times 100$$ **Maximum marks: 2**

8. This is an open ended question

1 mark: The student has demonstrated, at an
appropriate level, a limited understanding of the
chemistry involved. The candidate has made some
statement(s) at which is/are relevant to the situation,
showing that at least a little of the chemistry within the
problem is understood.

2 marks: The student has demonstrated, at an
appropriate level, a reasonable understanding of
the chemistry involved. The student makes some
statement(s) which is/are relevant to the situation,
showing that the problem is understood.

3 marks: The maximum available mark would be
awarded to a student who has demonstrated, at an
appropriate level, a good understanding of the chemistry
involved. The student shows a good comprehension
of the chemistry of the situation and has provided a
logically correct answer to the question posed. This
type of response might include a statement of the
principles involved, a relationship or an equation, and
the application of these to respond to the problem.
This does not mean the answer has to be what might be
termed an 'excellent' answer or a 'complete' one.

Maximum marks: 3

9. (a) (i) A drawing similar to

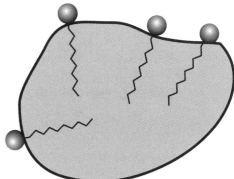

Diagram shows **at least one** detergent molecule.
All tails shown should be **fully** inside the
fat-soluble dirt.   **(1 mark)**

(ii) hydrophobic   **(1 mark)**

(b) (i) To break down coloured compounds/removes
stains/kill bacteria/kill fungi/inactivate viruses/
germs   **(1 mark)**

(ii) 18 cm³/0·018 litres **with correct unit** **(3 marks)**

Partial marking — 1 mark can be awarded for
two of the three steps shown below correctly
calculated:

1. number of moles of H_2O_2
2. mole ratio applied
3. calculated number of moles of O_2 multiplied
by 24 (24000)

If processed by proportion

68 g ⟷ 24 l (24000 cm³)

1 mark

OR

0·051 g ⟷ 0·036 l (36 cm³)

1 mark

1 mark for correct units.   **Maximum marks: 3**

(c) (i) amino acids   **(1 mark)**

(ii) (A) Amide/amide link/peptide link   **(1 mark)**

(B) Any of the shown amino acids:

(1 mark)

(iii) (A) Denaturing (1 mark)

(B) Temperature increase/pH (1 mark)

(d) (i) Condensation (1 mark)

(ii)

(1 mark)

10. (a) (i) 40·23/40·2/40 (%) (1 mark)

(ii) geranyl acetate/peak 5 (1 mark)

(b) 2·7p/3p

Partial marking — 1 mark can be awarded for:

Evidence of scaling up to 500 cm³

eg 460 mg of 1,8-cineole

OR

Evidence for determining a correct cost for a calculated mass of 1,8-cineole

eg 0·92 mg costs 0·00544 pence **Maximum marks: 2**

(c) (i)

(1 mark)

(ii) $C_{15}H_{24}$ OR $(C_5H_8)_3$ (1 mark)

HIGHER CHEMISTRY 2018

Section 1

Question	Answer	Max Mark
1.	B	1
2.	A	1
3.	D	1
4.	C	1
5.	D	1
6.	C	1
7.	A	1
8.	D	1
9.	A	1
10.	B	1
11.	D	1
12.	D	1
13.	A	1
14.	A	1
15.	D	1
16.	C	1
17.	B	1
18.	C	1
19.	B	1
20.	B	1

Section 2

1. (a) (i) Electronegativity is the measure of attraction an atom/nucleus has for the electrons in a bond/ shared electrons. (1 mark)

(ii) (More shells) so increased shielding/more shielding.

OR

Covalent radius increases/atom size increases/ more shells so attraction of the nucleus/protons for the (outer/shared) electrons decreases. (1 mark)

(b) (Intermolecular) forces/bonds increase (going down the group). (1)

LDFs are the forces (broken) between the molecules. (1)

The more electrons the stronger the LDFs. **(1)**
Maximum mark: 3

2. (a) Increasing number of protons (in the nucleus).

OR

Increasing/greater/stronger/higher nuclear charge
(holds electrons more tightly). **(1 mark)**

(b) (i) Sulfur chloride should be circled. **(1 mark)**

(ii) Silicon tetrachloride and hexane are non-polar. **(1)**

Silicon tetrachloride is non-polar due to its
shape/dipoles/polarities cancelling out. **(1)**
Maximum mark: 2

(c) (i) Silicon nitride is a (covalent) network. **(1)**

(Strong) covalent bonds are broken. **(1)**
Maximum mark: 2

(ii) 17·934/17·93/17·9/18 (%) **(2 marks)**

Partial mark for correct use of atom
economy relationship without correct use of
stoichiometry (working must be shown).

Partial marks

Correct working with no correct answer given.

$$\frac{140 \cdot 3}{(3 \times 170 \cdot 1) + (16 \times 17 \cdot 0)} \times 100$$

$$\frac{140 \cdot 3}{510 \cdot 3 + 272 \cdot 0} \times 100$$

$$\frac{140 \cdot 3}{782 \cdot 3} \times 100$$

Incorrect use of stoichiometry.

$$\frac{140 \cdot 3}{170 \cdot 1 + 17 \cdot 0} \times 100 = 74 \cdot 99$$

$$\frac{140 \cdot 3}{3 \times 170 \cdot 1 + 17 \cdot 0} \times 100 = 26 \cdot 6$$

$$\frac{140 \cdot 3}{170 \cdot 1 + 16 \times 17 \cdot 0} \times 100 = 31 \cdot 7$$

Answer and working must be shown.

0·179 **(1 mark)**

(d) (i) Diagram shows a workable method for the
passing of chlorine gas over heated aluminium.

Aluminium must be labelled and there must
be an indication of heat. Heated aluminium
accepted. **(1)**

Diagram allows aluminium chloride to be
collected **in a flask** as a solid and chlorine gas
to escape. **(1)**
Maximum mark: 2

(ii) To provide (initial) activation energy/
(sufficient) energy to form activated
(activation) complex. **(1 mark)**

3. (a) Heating mantle or hot plate
OR
(hot) water bath. **(1 mark)**

(b) Condense reactants or products/acts as a
condenser/to prevent escape of (volatile/gaseous)

reactants or products/to prevent the escape of
gas(es). **(1 mark)**

(c) (i) Water (Accept formula H_2O) **(1 mark)**

(ii) Correctly calculates number of moles of:
Benzoic acid = 0·041
Methanol = 0·078.
OR
Working out that 1·31 g of methanol would be
needed to react with 5 g of benzoic acid.
OR
Working out that 9·53 g of benzoic acid would
be needed to react with 2·5 g of methanol. **(1)**
Statement demonstrating understanding of
limiting reactant

e.g. there are less moles of benzoic acid
therefore it is the limiting reactant.
OR
There are more moles of methanol therefore it
is in excess.
OR
0·078 moles of methanol would require 0·078
moles of benzoic acid. **(1)**
Maximum mark: 2

(iii) (£)12·84 **(2)**
Partial Marks
Mass benzoic acid = 161·3(g).
OR
Cost to make 3·1g of methyl benzoate = (£) 0·398.
OR
Evidence of a calculated mass of benzoic
acid × 7·96 or 8 (p). **(1)**
Maximum mark: 2

4. (a) Correctly drawn structure of pentan-2-one,
pentan-3-one or 3-methylbutanone.
(Accept full or shortened structural formulae)
Maximum mark: 1

(b) Fehling's solution/Tollens' reagent/**acidified**
dichromate solution. **(1 mark)**

(c) Permanent dipole-permanent dipole (interactions/
attractions). **(1 mark)**

(d) Will react with oxygen/undergo oxidation. **(1)**

Forming a **carboxylic** acid (which has unpleasant
taste). **(1)**
Maximum mark: 2

(e) (i) Because it has two molecules joining together with the loss of a small/water molecule.

(1 mark)

(ii) 6-methylheptan-2-one **(1 mark)**

5. This is an open ended question

1 mark: The student has demonstrated, at an appropriate level, a limited understanding of the chemistry involved. The candidate has made some statement(s) which is/are relevant to the situation, showing that at least a little of the chemistry within the problem is understood.

2 marks: The student has demonstrated, at an appropriate level, a reasonable understanding of the chemistry involved. The student makes some statement(s) which is/are relevant to the situation, showing that the problem is understood.

3 marks: The maximum available mark would be awarded to a student who has demonstrated, at an appropriate level, a good understanding of the chemistry involved. The student shows a good comprehension of the chemistry of the situation and has provided a logically correct answer to the question posed. This type of response might include a statement of the principles involved, a relationship or an equation, and the application of these to respond to the problem. This does not mean the answer has to be what might be termed an 'excellent' answer or a 'complete' one.

Maximum mark: 3

6. (a) (i) (enzyme) hydrolysis **(1 mark)**

(ii) $C_{20}H_{29}OH$
OR
$C_{20}H_{30}O$ **(1 mark)**

(b) (i) Bond breaking by UV (light) or example of initiation reaction (equation or diagram).

e.g. chlorine splitting to give two free radicals is accepted, provided UV is shown. **(1 mark)**

(ii) propagation **(1 mark)**

(iii) Can react with free radicals forming stable molecules/free radicals (and prevent chain reactions).

OR

Donates electron(s).

OR

Acting as a reducing agent.

OR

Provide electrons to pair with an unpaired electron. **(1 mark)**

(c) (i) Circle any peptide link (CONH). **(1 mark)**

(ii) **(1 mark)**

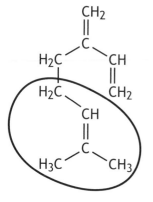

7. (a) (i) **(1 mark)**

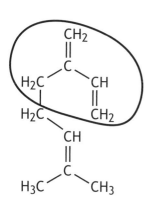

(ii) Sesquiterpene **(1 mark)**

(b) (i) 5·345/5.35/5.3 (kg) **(2)**
Partial marking
Mass of squalene
= 10·69 × 500 000
= 5 345 000 (mg) **(1)**
OR
For incorrectly calculating mass in mg but correctly converting to kg. **(1)**
OR
For incorrectly calculating mass of squalene but correctly multiplying this by 500 000. **(1)**
OR
Conversion of 10·69 mg to kg
i.e. 10·69 × 10⁻⁶. **(1)**

Maximum mark: 2

(ii) 6/six (moles) **(1 mark)**

(c) (i) Addition
OR
hydration. **(1 mark)**

(ii) (terpineol) is a tertiary alcohol (and cannot be oxidised). **(1 mark)**

8. (a) 286 (kJ mol⁻¹) **(2)**
Partial mark 1 mark
Evidence of the use of **all** the correct bond enthalpies (or correct multiples thereof) (412, 348, 838, 436 (ignore signs)).
OR
If only three values are retrieved, the candidate recognises that bond breaking is endothermic and bond formation is exothermic and correctly manipulates the bond enthalpy values they have used to give their answer. **Maximum mark: 2**

(b) (+) 185 (kJ mol^{-1}) **(2 marks)**

[(−1182) + (−572) + (+1939)]

= (+) 185 (kJ mol^{-1})

Partial marks

Treat as two concepts. Either would be acceptable for 1 mark.

Evidence of understanding of reversal of third enthalpy value

i.e. +1939 or 1939 must be seen.

The other two enthalpy values (regardless of value) **must** be negative, or this partial mark cannot be awarded.

OR

Evidence of understanding of multiplying the first enthalpy value by 3 and the second enthalpy value by 2.

Ignore the enthalpy signs associated with these numbers

i.e. any combination of

3 (±394) **and** 2 (±286)

OR

±1182 **and** ±572

Multiplication of the third enthalpy value by any factor is taken as cancelling of this partial mark.

Maximum mark: 2

(c) (i) 48475 (kJ) (Also accepted: −48475 (kJ))
(1 mark)

(ii) 13·76/13·8/14 (g) **(2 marks)**

Partial mark 1 mark

Mass of oxygen required = 3·2 (g)

OR

550·4 (g) **Maximum marks: 2**

(iii) Methanol and ethanol contain oxygen in their structure, (so less additional oxygen is required). **(1 mark)**

9. (a) (i) **1 mark each** for any two of the following points.
- recycle (waste) gases
- use catalyst
- low/reduce energy requirements
- reactors are run at low temperatures/the temperatures in the reactors is lowered
- inexpensive feedstocks
- selling/using by-products **(2 marks)**

(ii) (fractional) distillation **(1 mark)**

(b) Propan-1-ol has fewer hydroxyl groups than ethane-1,2-diol/ethane-1,2-diol has more hydroxyl groups/propan-1-ol has 1 hydroxyl group and ethane-1,2-diol has 2. **(1)**

Weaker/fewer hydrogen bonds between propan-1-ol molecules.

OR

Stronger/more hydrogen bonds between ethane-1,2-diol molecules. **(1)**

Maximum marks: 2

(c) Structure of propane-1,2-diol or propane-1,3-diol or propane-1,1-diol or propane-2,2-diol. **(1 mark)**

(d) (i) Pipette (used to measure 20 cm^3 of ethanol.) **(1)**

Statement of use of **volumetric/standard** flask to make up to/fill to the mark/to 100 cm^3. **(1)**

Maximum marks: 2

(ii) 157·5(cm^3) **(1 mark)**

(iii) (A) **(1 mark)**

(iii) (B) Correct molecular formula (NaC$_2$H$_3$O$_3$)

OR

shortened structural formula (HOCH$_2$COONa)

OR

any full structural formula which shows the correct salt. **(1 mark)**

10. This is an open ended question

    1 mark: The student has demonstrated, at an appropriate level, a limited understanding of the chemistry involved. The candidate has made some statement(s) which is/are relevant to the situation, showing that at least a little of the chemistry within the problem is understood.

    2 marks: The student has demonstrated, at an appropriate level, a reasonable understanding of the chemistry involved. The student makes some statement(s) which is/are relevant to the situation, showing that the problem is understood.

    3 marks: The maximum available mark would be awarded to a student who has demonstrated, at an appropriate level, a good understanding of the chemistry involved. The student shows a good comprehension of the chemistry of the situation and has provided a logically correct answer to the question posed. This type of response might include a statement of the principles involved, a relationship or an equation, and the application of these to respond to the problem. This does not mean the answer has to be what might be termed an 'excellent' answer or a 'complete' one.   **Maximum mark: 3**

11. (a) Correct description of weighing by difference.
    OR
    Correct description of use of the Tare function.
                                              (1 mark)

    (b) $2I^- (aq) \rightarrow I_2(aq) + 2e^-$
    OR
    $2I^- (aq) \rightarrow I_2(s) + 2e^-$ **(1 mark)**

    (c) (i) $9\cdot5(cm^3)$ **(1 mark)**

        (ii) $4\cdot75 \times 10^{-6}$ moles   **(2 marks)**
        Partial mark for correct use of mole ratio.
        OR
        Determination of number of moles without using the mole ratio.   **Maximum marks: 2**

12. (a) (i) More/adding chlorine(s).   **(1)**
        More/adding carbon(s).
        OR
        Adding an alkyl/hydrocarbon chain/group.
        OR
        Longer/bigger carbon/hydrocarbon/alkyl (chain/group).   **(1)**
                                              (2 marks)

        (ii) 2-chloro-4,5-dimethylphenol   **(1 mark)**

    (b) (i) $126\cdot9/127(kg)$
        Partial mark either for:
        Calculation of the theoretical yield 141 (no unit required)   **(1)**
        OR
        for correctly calculating 90% of an incorrectly calculated theoretical yield.   **(1)**
                                              (2 marks)

        (ii) Propanone
        OR
        Acetone
        OR
        Propan-2-one.   **(1 mark)**

Section 1

Question	Answer	Max Mark
1.	A	1
2.	D	1
3.	B	1
4.	C	1
5.	B	1
6.	C	1
7.	D	1
8.	D	1
9.	A	1
10.	B	1
11.	B	1
12.	C	1
13.	B	1
14.	A	1
15.	C	1
16.	A	1
17.	C	1
18.	C	1
19.	B	1
20.	D	1
21.	A	1
22.	A	1
23.	A	1
24.	D	1
25.	B	1

Section 2

1. (a) (i) Boron
        OR
        Carbon
        OR
        B
        OR
        C   **(1 mark)**

        (ii) Increasing/greater/stronger/higher nuclear charge
        OR
        Increasing/greater/higher number of protons
                                              (1 mark)

        (iii) Lithium
        OR
        Li   **(1 mark)**

    (b) Electrons are further from the nucleus
        OR
        Atomic size increases

OR

Extra energy level (1)

Increased screening/shielding (1)

Maximum marks: 2

(c) Covalent molecular (1 mark)

2. (a) Award up to 3 marks for answers containing the following points:

Br_2 non-polar/I-Cl polar

OR

ICl has permanent dipole- permanent dipole interactions (1)

Br_2 and ICl have same number of electrons

OR

Strength of LDF Br_2 and ICl similar (1)

Boiling point of ICl higher than boiling point of Br_2

OR

Intermolecular forces are broken when a substance boils (1)

Maximum marks: 3

(b) H_2/hydrogen (1 mark)

(c) (i) Cl–H + H· (1)

H–H / H_2 (1)

Maximum marks: 2

(ii) To prevent light/UV shining on sample

OR

To prevent initiation

OR

To prevent radicals from forming

OR

To prevent (glass/tube) shattering (1 mark)

(iii) −185 (kJ mol^{-1}) (2 marks)

Partial marking:

A single mark is available if either of the following operations is correctly executed.

EITHER

The three relevant bond enthalpy values are retrieved; 436, 243 and 432

OR

Correct use of incorrect bond enthalpy values

(d) $10Cl^-(aq) + 2MnO_4^-(aq) + 16H^+(aq)$
↓
$5Cl_2(g) + 2Mn^{2+}(aq) + 8H_2O(\ell)$ (1 mark)

3. (a) (i) (A) Butyl propanoate (1 mark)

(B) B>A>C (1 mark)

(ii) (A) Carbonyl (1 mark)

(B) (1 mark)

(b) Any one of the four following groups of atoms circled

(1 mark)

(c) (i) Award up to 3 marks for the following points:

Sodium lauryl sulfate has both hydrophobic/oil-soluble and hydrophilic/water-soluble parts

OR

Sodium lauryl sulfate has both ionic and non-polar parts (1)

Correct identification of the parts of this molecule which dissolve in water and oil (1)

Formation (by agitation) of a 'balllike' structure/globule (with the oil/grease held inside the ball) or micelle or mention of an emulsion (1)

Repulsion of micelles (due to negatively charged heads) (1)

Maximum marks: 3

(ii) Do not form scum/precipitates (with hard water) **(1 mark)**

(d) **Award 1 mark** where the candidate has demonstrated, at an appropriate level, a limited understanding of the chemistry involved. They have made some statement(s) which are relevant to the situation, showing that they have understood at least a little of the chemistry within the problem.

Award 2 marks where the candidate has demonstrated, at an appropriate level, a reasonable understanding of the chemistry involved. They make some statement(s) which are relevant to the situation, showing that they have understood the problem.

Award 3 marks where the candidate has demonstrated, at an appropriate level, a good understanding of the chemistry involved. They show a good comprehension of the chemistry of the situation and provide a logically correct answer to the question posed. This type of response might include a statement of the principles involved, a relationship or an equation, and the application of these to respond to the problem. The answer does not need to be 'excellent' or 'complete' for the candidate to gain full marks.

Award 0 marks where the candidate has not demonstrated, at an appropriate level, an understanding of the chemistry involved. There is no evidence that they have recognised the area of chemistry involved, or they have not given any statement of a relevant chemistry principle. Award this mark also if the candidate merely restates the chemistry given in the question. **Maximum marks: 3**

4. (a) (i) Shea butter has fewer double bonds/is not very unsaturated (1)

Unsaturated molecules cannot pack tightly

OR

Saturated molecules can pack tightly (1)

The London dispersion forces/van der Waals' forces between its molecules are stronger (than in oils) (1)

Maximum marks: 3

(ii) 139 − 149 **(1 mark)**

(b) (i) Glycerol/propane-1,2,3-triol **(1 mark)**

(ii) 24·8 or 25 (%) **(3 marks)**

Partial marking:

Calculation of theoretical yield of soap omitting mole ratio (1·72 (g))

OR

Correctly calculated number of moles of reactant **and** product; 0·00566 and 0·00421 **(1)**

Use of correct mole ratio 1:3 **(1)**

Correctly calculated % yield using the actual mass and an incorrectly calculated theoretical mass

OR

Correctly calculated % yield using incorrectly calculated numbers of moles of product and reactant **(1)**

5. (a) −43·9 (kJ mol^{-1}) **(2 marks)**

Partial marking:

Evidence of understanding of reversal of first **and** final equations, with second equation unchanged **(1)**

(b) (i) (£) 1045 **(2 marks)**

Partial marking:

A single mark is available if any one of the following operations is correctly executed.

Calculating the cost of the reactants required to prepare 5·75 g of butan2ol: £60·11

OR

Calculating the mass of both reactants needed to produce 100 g of butan-2-ol: 87·1 g of propanal and 347·8 g of CH_3MgBr

OR

Having incorrectly calculated the cost of the reactants required to prepare 5·75 g of butan-2-ol, correctly scaling their calculated cost by 100/5·75 to obtain the cost to produce 100 g of butan-2-ol

(ii) Hexan-2-ol **(1 mark)**
(Accept 2-hexanol)

(c) (i) Oxidation **(1 mark)**

(ii) −3 (°C) **(1 mark)**

6. (a) Shape maintained by intermolecular bonds (between side chains on protein) (1)

These bonds broken when the protein is heated (1)

Maximum marks: 2

(b) (i) Gentle method of heating

OR

Can control temperature easily

OR

To prevent the protein structure changing/ denaturing

OR

Mention of flammability **(1 mark)**

(ii) Sodium oxide

OR

Sodium hydroxide

OR

Sodium carbonate

OR

Sodium hydrogen carbonate **(1 mark)**

(iii)   **(1 mark)**

OR

OR

(c) 4 or 4·0 (mg)   **(1 mark)**

(d) Eight or 8   **(1 mark)**

7. (a) Carboxyl (group)   **(1 mark)**

   OR

   Carboxylic acid (group)

(b) (i) 100 (%)   **(1 mark)**

   (ii) Curve starting at the level representing the reactants and finishing at the level representing the products but with a maximum, or maxima, below the existing maximum   **(1 mark)**

(c) (i) Large hydrocarbon section/non-polar chain (attached to the carboxyl group)   **(1 mark)**

   (ii) (A) (It is an) emulsifier
       OR
       To stop layers forming   **(1 mark)**

   (B) 2·5 (cm³)   **(1 mark)**

8. (a) Any correctly drawn diagram showing an oxygen atom attracted to a hydrogen atom within a hydroxyl group/water e.g.

OR

                                         (1 mark)

(b)   **(1 mark)**

$$CH_3 - \underset{\underset{CH_3}{|}}{CH} - CH_2 - OH$$

(c) 12 200 cm³ or 12·2 litres

Partial marking:

Where the correct value for the volume has not been calculated, one mark is available for either:

The correct strategy to calculate the mass of 2-methylpropan-1-ol required: $\frac{351000}{36 \cdot 1}$ or 9720

OR

The correct strategy to work out the volume of 2-methylpropan-1-ol required: *mass in g* × 1·25 or $\frac{351000}{28 \cdot 88}$

OR

A correct strategy to work out the energy released per cm³: $\frac{36 \cdot 1}{1 \cdot 25}$ or 28·88

One mark is also available where the candidate gives the correct unit for volume in their final answer.

9. (a) (i) A solution of exactly/accurately/precisely known concentration   **(1 mark)**

   (ii) 221 (mg)   **(2 marks)**

   Partial marking:

   A single mark is available if any one of the following operations is correctly executed.
   The GFM of NaF has been calculated correctly: 42 (g)
   OR
   The number of moles of fluoride ions has been calculated correctly: 0·00526

   (iii) Dissolve (sample) in a small/minimum volume of (deionised) water   **(1)**

   Transfer with rinsings   **(1)**

   Make up to the mark in a volumetric/standard flask   **(1)**

                    Maximum marks: 3

   (iv) (Tap water) might contain fluoride ions.
       OR
       (Tap water) might contain species that interfere with the reaction.

OR

(Tap water) might be coloured. **(1 mark)**

(v) $1.5 - 2.0$ (mg l^{-1}) **(1 mark)**

(b) (i) Pipette **(1 mark)**

(ii) 0.0324 (mol l^{-1}) **(3 marks)**

Partial marking:

Two 'concept' marks are available.

For correct use of the relationship between concentration, number of moles and volume:

e.g. by calculating a number of moles by multiplying a concentration by a volume and/or by calculating a concentration by dividing a number of moles by a volume, and/or calculating a number of moles

OR

For inserting correct pairings for c and v concentrations and volumes into the formula $\dfrac{c_1 v_1}{n_1} = \dfrac{c_2 v_2}{n_2}$ **(1)**

For appreciation that this reaction demonstrates a 2:5 stoichiometry: eg by multiplying a number of moles by either $\dfrac{2}{5}$ or $\dfrac{5}{2}$

OR

For substitution of the numbers 2 and 5 into as values for n in the formula $\dfrac{c_1 v_1}{n_1} = \dfrac{c_2 v_2}{n_2}$ **(1)**

10. (a) (i) When a molecule reacts with water to break down/apart (into smaller molecules) **(1 mark)**

(ii) Methanol **(1 mark)**

(iii) Essential (amino acids) **(1 mark)**

(b) (i) $69 - 70$ (mg) **(1 mark)**

(ii) Sample of **Y** should be diluted **(1 mark)**
OR
Less of sample **Y** should be used
OR
Smaller sample of **Y**

11. (a) $2NaOH + Cl_2 \rightarrow NaClO + NaCl + H_2O$ **(1 mark)**

(b) $ClO^- + 2H^+ + 2e^- \rightarrow Cl^- + H_2O$ **(1 mark)**

(c) (i) Gas-tight reaction vessel fitted with delivery tube **(1)**

Method for collecting and measuring the volume of gas produced **(1)**

Hydrogen peroxide, bleach and oxygen labelled in correct position **(1)**
Maximum marks: 3

(ii) 0.67 (mol l^{-1}) **(3 marks)**

Partial marking:

Correct use of the relationship between volume of gas and number of moles, e.g. a volume of oxygen, in whatever unit, being divided by the molar volume, in whatever unit **(1)**

Correct use of the relationship between the concentration of a solution, the number of moles of solute and the volume of solution, e.g. a value that the candidate believes to be the number of moles of ClO$^-$ divided by the volume of the solution, in whatever unit. **(1)**

12. (a) (i) Purple to colourless **(1 mark)**

(ii) 83 or 83.3 (s) **(2 marks)**

Partial marking:
A single mark is available if either of the following operations is correctly executed:
Reading rate correctly from graph: 0.012 (s^{-1})
OR
Correctly calculating the reaction time from an incorrect value for the relative rate.

(b) (i) The peak of the curve should be to the left and higher than the original peak. **(1 mark)**

(ii) A vertical line should have been drawn at a lower kinetic energy than the original Ea shown on graph. **(1 mark)**

(c) Incorrect orientation/geometry **(1 mark)**
OR
Activated complex breaks up to reform the reactants

13. **Award 1 mark** where the candidate has demonstrated, at an appropriate level, a limited understanding of the chemistry involved. They have made some statement(s) which are relevant to the situation, showing that they have understood at least a little of the chemistry within the problem.

Award 2 marks where the candidate has demonstrated, at an appropriate level, a reasonable understanding of the chemistry involved. They make some statement(s) which are relevant to the situation, showing that they have understood the problem.

Award 3 marks where the candidate has demonstrated, at an appropriate level, a good understanding of the chemistry involved. They show a good comprehension of the chemistry of the situation and provide a logically correct answer to the question posed. This type of response might include a statement of the principles involved, a relationship or an equation, and the application of these to respond to the problem. The answer does not need to be 'excellent' or 'complete' for the candidate to gain full marks.

Award 0 marks where the candidate has not demonstrated, at an appropriate level, an understanding of the chemistry involved. There is no evidence that they have recognised the area of chemistry involved, or they have not given any statement of a relevant chemistry principle. Award this mark also if the candidate merely restates the chemistry given in the question. **Maximum mark: 3**